CGP has got Year 6 Science practice in the bag!

This brilliant CGP Workbook is the ideal way for pupils to develop their Year 6 Science skills.

It's packed with questions covering the Year 6 Programme of Study. We've also included quizzes at the end of every topic, and extension activities throughout the book to satisfy extra-curious pupils.

And if that wasn't enough, there's also an End of Year Test to make sure everything's sunk in. Plus, answers to all the questions are included at the back of the book. Perfect!

What CGP is all about

Our sole aim here at CGP is to produce the highest quality books — carefully written, immaculately presented and dangerously close to being funny.

Then we work our socks off to get them out to you — at the cheapest possible prices.

Published by CGP

Editors:
Mary Falkner, Josie Gilbert, Rachael Rogers and George Wright

Contributor:
Paddy Gannon

ISBN: 978 1 78908 887 8

With thanks to Susan Alexander, Duncan Lindsay and Glenn Rogers for the proofreading.
With thanks to Jan Greenway for the copyright research.

Printed by Elanders Ltd, Newcastle upon Tyne.

Clipart from Corel®

Illustrations by: Sandy Gardner Artist, email sandy@sandygardner.co.uk

Based on the classic CGP style created by Richard Parsons.

Contents

Topic 1 – Living Things and Their Habitats

Topic 2 – Animals Including Humans

Topic 3 – Evolution and Inheritance

Topic 4 – Light

Topic 5 – Electricity

Grouping Organisms

Organisms have different features which you can use to sort them into groups.

1 **Draw lines to match each animal to the correct group.**

Vertebrate	Invertebrate

snail eagle frog crab shark

2 **Write the names of the plants below into the correct places in the table.**

	Found in ponds and lakes	Grows several metres high
Flowering	....	....
Non-flowering	....	....

3 **Look at the organisms in the box.**

Describe one feature that the organisms have in common and one feature that is different for the two organisms.

Feature in common: ....

....

Feature that is different: ....

....

Grouping Organisms

4 **Prakash is using a microscope to look at a micro-organism.**

He knows that micro-organisms in group A cause a particular disease, and micro-organisms in groups B and C are harmless.

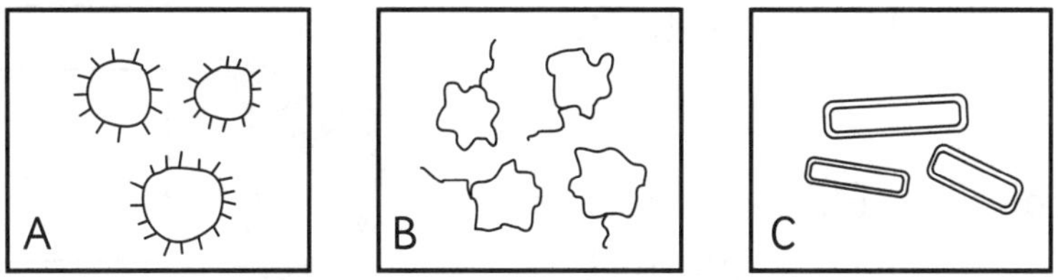

A B C

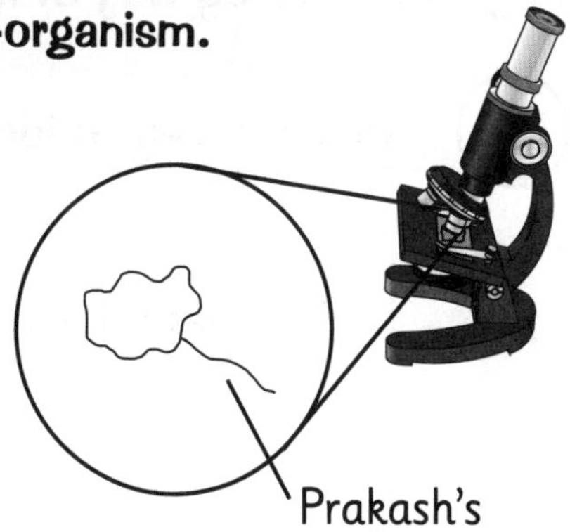

Prakash's micro-organism

Do you think Prakash's micro-organism would cause the disease? Explain your answer.

....

....

5 **Jazzy is observing some unknown animals. From the options given below, write down which group you would expect each animal to be in.**

Insect | Fish | Bird | Amphibian | Reptile

This animal has wings and its body has three parts. ....

This animal lays eggs and has feathers. ....

This animal has scales and lays its eggs on land. ....

Now Try This

Ask some friends or family members to name vertebrates until you have a list of ten different ones. Sort the animals into birds, fish, amphibians, reptiles and mammals. Then think about the differences between animals in the same group — can you think of ways you could split them up further?

Classification Keys

Keys are a handy way of identifying what exactly it is that you're looking at...

1 **Use this key to identify the animals.**

1) Does it have wings? YES — it's a dove
NO — go to 2)

2) Does it have scales? YES — it's a carp
NO — go to 3)

3) Is it stripy? YES — it's a zebra
NO — it's a sloth

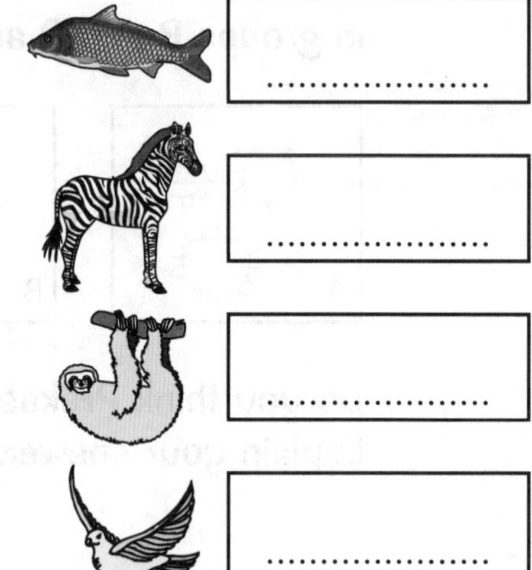

2 **Fill in the names of the organisms on this key.**

wheat  lizard  spider  apple tree  worm

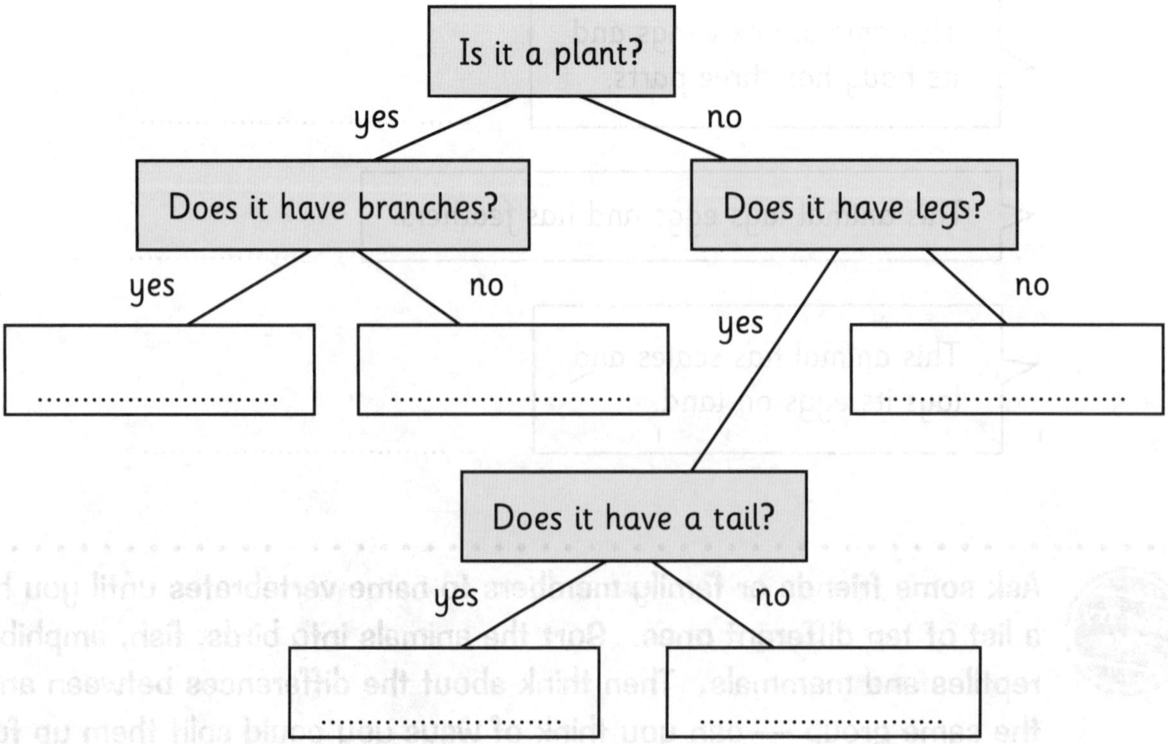

Is it a plant?
- yes → Does it have branches?
  - yes → ....
  - no → ....
- no → Does it have legs?
  - yes → Does it have a tail?
    - yes → ....
    - no → ....
  - no → ....

Classification Keys

3 **Create your own key for these animals by filling in the boxes.**

Think about the different ways you could split the animals up. For example, the number of legs, whether it has scales, fur, feathers, or other features that stand out. There is more than one way you could create the key.

python

chameleon

cheetah

flamingo

polar bear

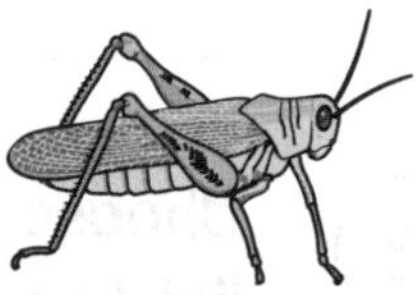

cricket

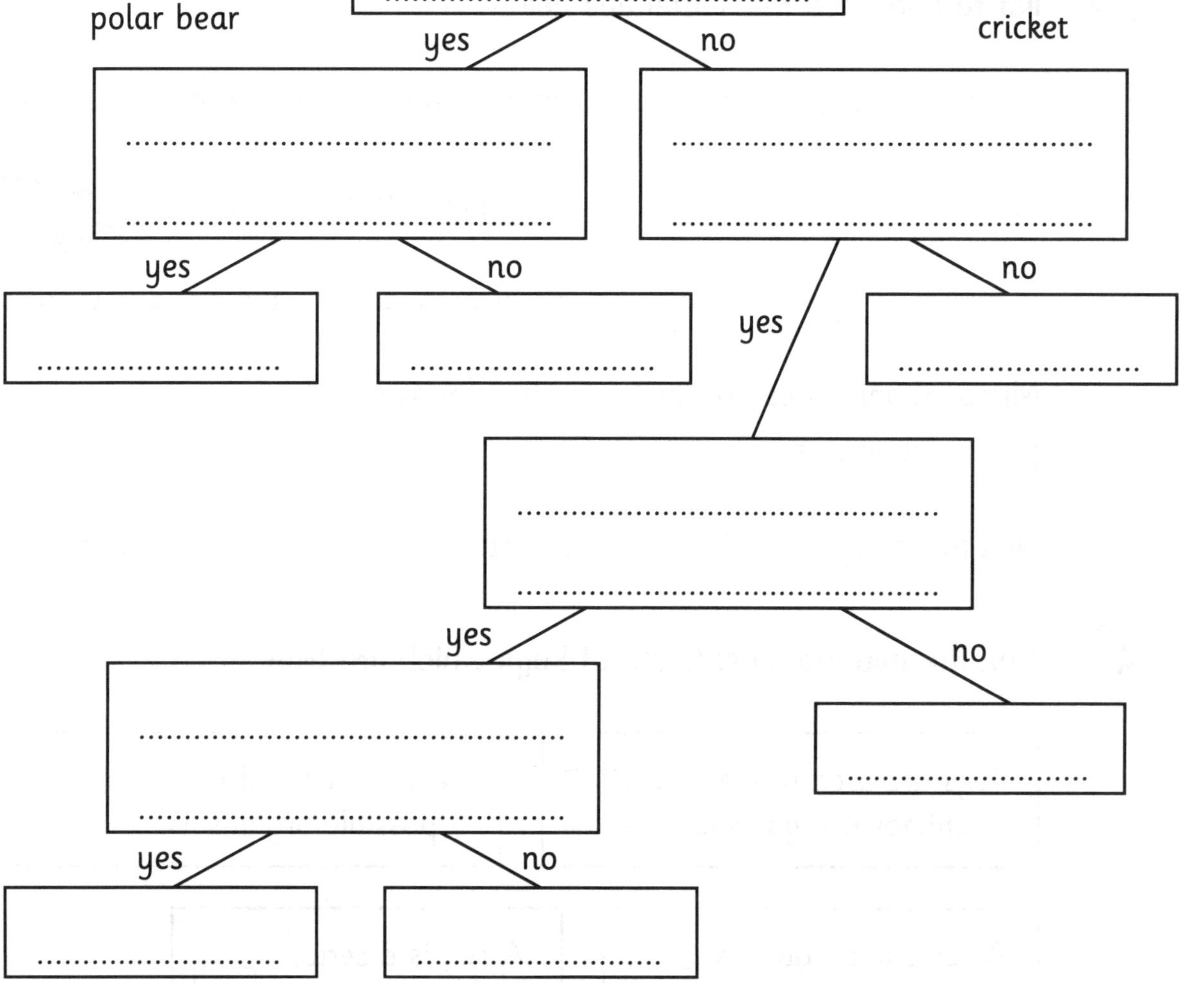

....
....

yes / no

....
....

....
....

yes / no

....
....

yes / no

....

....
....

yes / no

....
....

....

yes / no

....
....

Choose a habitat (e.g. woodland, ocean, mountain) and find pictures of at least five organisms that live there. Create a key that someone could use to identify these organisms. Ask a friend or family member to test your key to see if it works.

End of Topic Quiz

That's the first topic out of the way — time to test your knowledge.

1 What are the three main groups of living things?

1. .... 2. .... 3. ....

3 marks

2 What is an invertebrate? Give an example.

....

....

2 marks

3 Choose the correct words from the list to complete the sentences below.

bacteria | algae | flowering | invertebrate | vertebrate | coniferous | fish

Tigers are .... animals with four legs.

.... plants include grasses, cereals and deciduous trees.

Micro-organisms can be split into the groups of ...., fungi and viruses.

Non-flowering plants include moss and .... trees.

4 marks

4 Tick the two statements about keys which are true.

- Keys are used to identify unknown organisms. ☐
- Keys are limited to four possible organisms. ☐
- A key should always take the form of a branched pattern ☐
- A key is a series of questions with yes/no answers. ☐

2 marks

Score: ☐/11

The Human Body

To keep working, your body relies on loads of different organs with different jobs.

1 Unscramble the words below and write them in the correct places on the diagram.

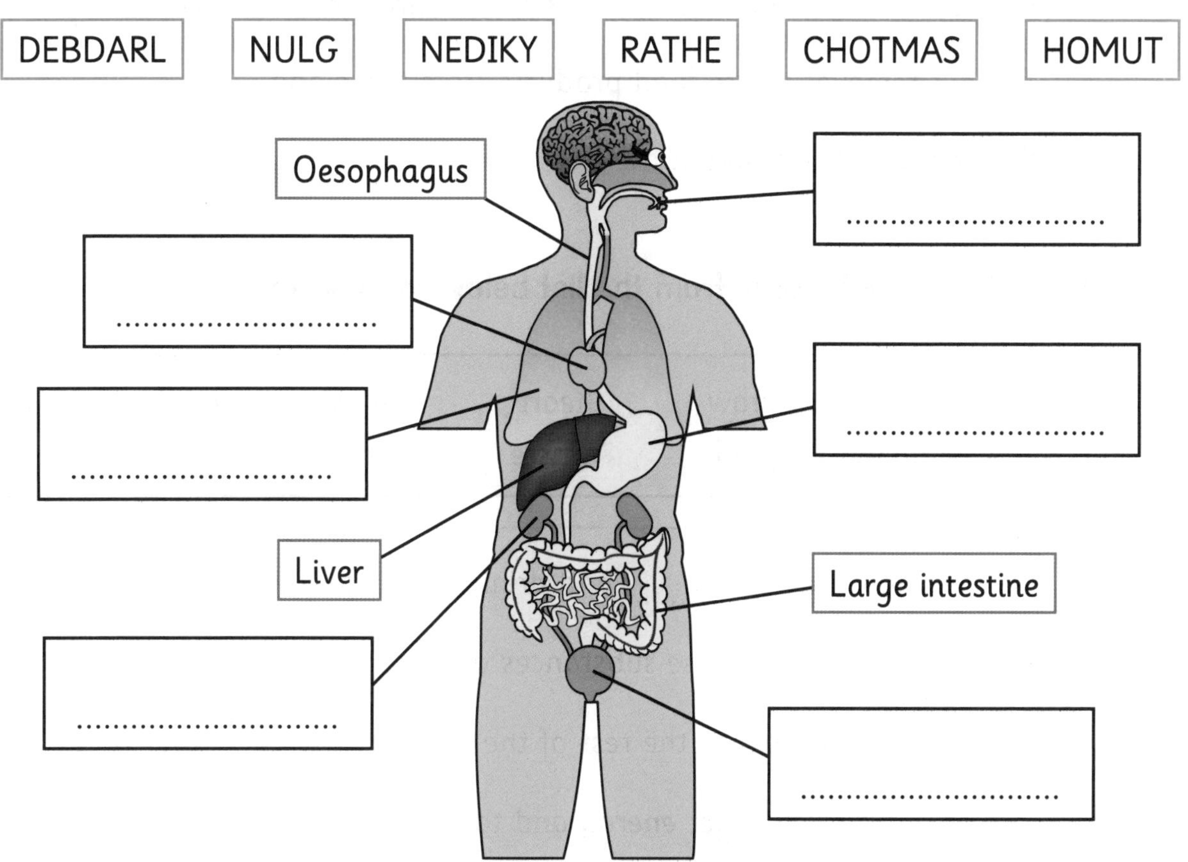

2 Draw a line to match each word below to the best description of it.

Muscles	These make up the skeleton, which helps the body stand upright.
Joints	These always work in pairs where one contracts and one relaxes.
Bones	These are areas of the skeleton that allow it to move.
Ribs	These protect the heart and lungs.

The diagram on this page is a big one, with lots of labels. Try to draw the diagram yourself and add all of the labels. Add a few words to your labels to describe what each organ does.

Transport in the Body

Your blood gets food, water and oxygen to every part of your body. Pretty handy...

1 **Write T or F to show whether the statements below are true or false.**

Vitamins and minerals get into the blood through the kidneys. ....

The gut removes waste food products from the blood. ....

Water enters the blood in the gut. ....

2 **Pick the right words from the list below to fill in the gaps.**

eyes	grow	heart	lungs	body	water
kidneys	food	waste	eat	blood	urine

When you .... and drink, your body takes in food and .... These substances get into your ...., which carries them to the rest of the .... Your body uses .... to get energy and to help you .... Your blood also carries .... back to your .... and kidneys. The .... help to get rid of waste food products and water.

3 **Shona says: "The lungs are great! They help you take in the carbon dioxide you need and get rid of waste oxygen."**

Explain why Shona is wrong.

....

....

Research how frogs, cats and crabs transport things around their bodies. Do they have lungs, blood and a digestive system like a human does? If not, how do they get the things they need into their bodies?

Circulation

'Circulation' is all about blood moving around, and around, and around your body.

1 **Circle the three parts of the circulatory system.**

mouth intestines blood joints lungs

heart toes rib cage blood vessels

2 **Write down four things that are carried around the body in the blood.**

1. .... 3. ....

2. .... 4. ....

3 **Fill in the missing letters to complete this information about circulation.**

One job of the blood is to DE.....I.....ER food and O.....Y.....E..... to different parts of the body. The .....RG.....N..... of the body all have important functions and they need E.....E.....GY to be able to work properly. Our bodies get .....N.....R.....Y by using up .....OO..... and .....X.....GE..... — this means our organs all need B.....OO..... to provide these ingredients so they keep WO.....K.....N..... .

Ravi says that you can find blood vessels in every organ of the body. Using the completed information, give a reason why Ravi might say this.

....

....

The Heart

The heart is really important — it's what keeps the circulatory system going.

1 **Choose words from the box below to complete the labels on the diagram.**

muscle	lungs	gut	blood	body	brain	water

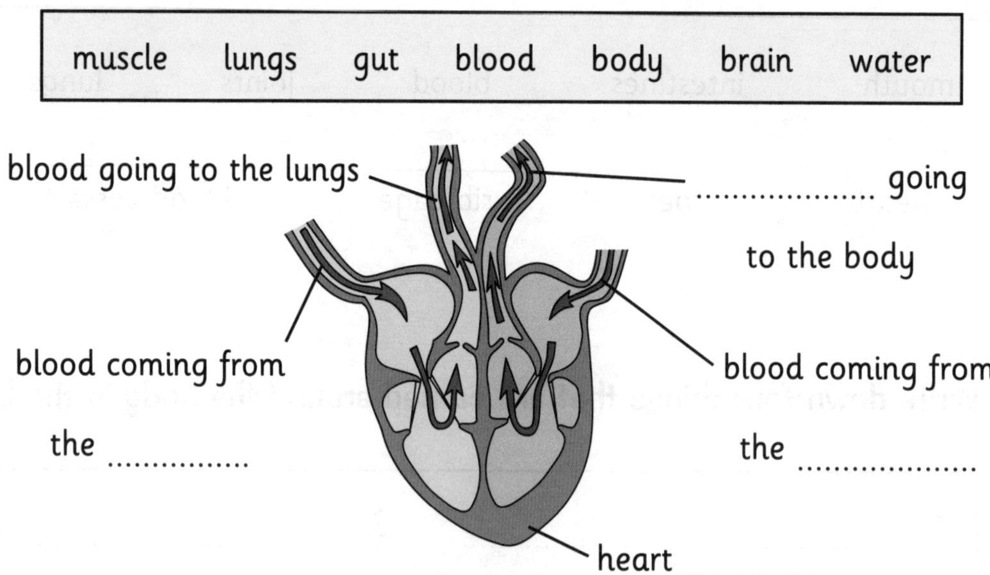

2 **Complete these sentences by circling the correct words in the brackets.**

Most of the heart is made up of **muscle / fat**, which allows it to act like a **pump / tap**.

When the muscles in the heart **contract / relax**, they squeeze **blood / air** out of the heart.

3 **When Ryan puts two fingers on his neck, he can feel a regular movement underneath his skin. This movement is called a pulse.**

Suggest why Ryan can feel this.

....

....

Put together a fact file about the human heart. You could include things like its size, shape and weight, how often it beats, and how to keep it healthy.

Blood and Blood Vessels

The tubes that your blood moves through as it circulates are called blood vessels.

1. **Fill in the box next to each sentence to say whether it is describing arteries, veins or capillaries.**

These blood vessels carry blood from the heart to different parts of the body.	....
These are tiny blood vessels that allow substances to move in and out of the blood.	....
These blood vessels carry blood back to the heart from other parts of the body.	....

2. **Write numbers in the boxes to put these sentences about the circulation of blood in the right order, starting with blood leaving the heart.**

- [ ] The heart pumps blood out through an artery.
- [ ] Blood containing waste products travels back to the heart through a vein.
- [ ] Blood enters capillaries in the muscle and delivers oxygen and food.
- [ ] Blood containing oxygen and food travels to a muscle.

3. **For each diagram, write down whether the arrow is pointing to an artery or a vein.**

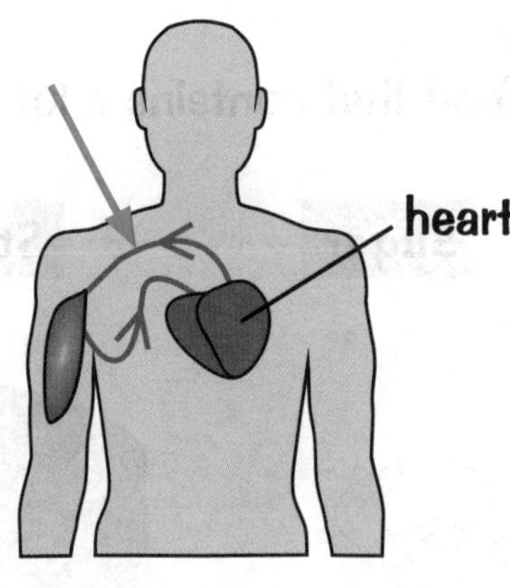

....

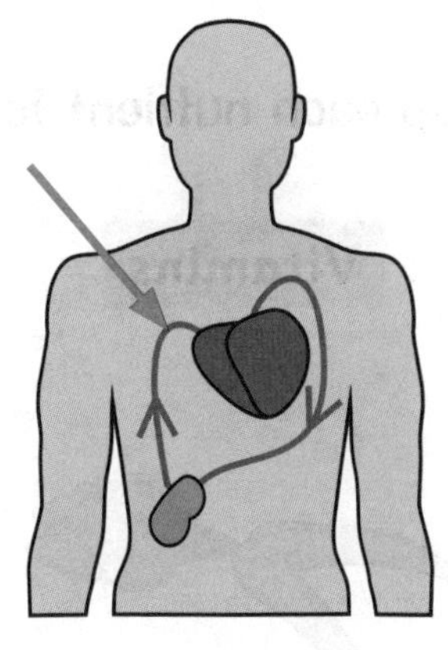

....

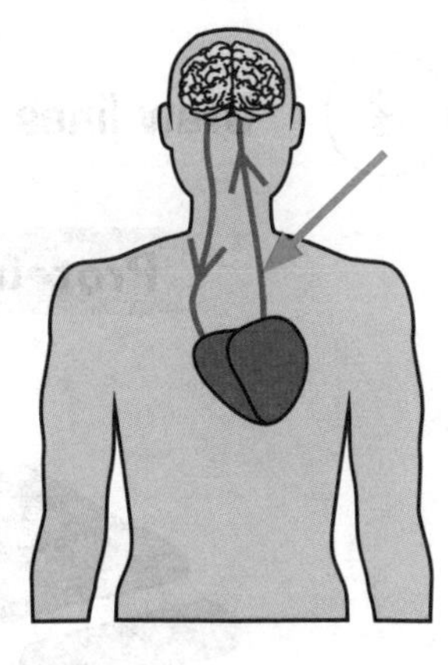

....

Eating Healthily

Eating healthily is really important — so here are two pages of questions about it.

1. **Tick the picture that shows the most balanced diet.**

2. **Put a cross in the box next to the sentence that is false.**

Vitamins and minerals are important nutrients for humans. ☐

Eating badly can make you feel tired and unwell. ☐

It doesn't matter what you eat, as long as it's not too much food. ☐

Explain why you think this sentence is false.

....

....

3. **Draw lines to match up each nutrient to the food that contains a lot of it.**

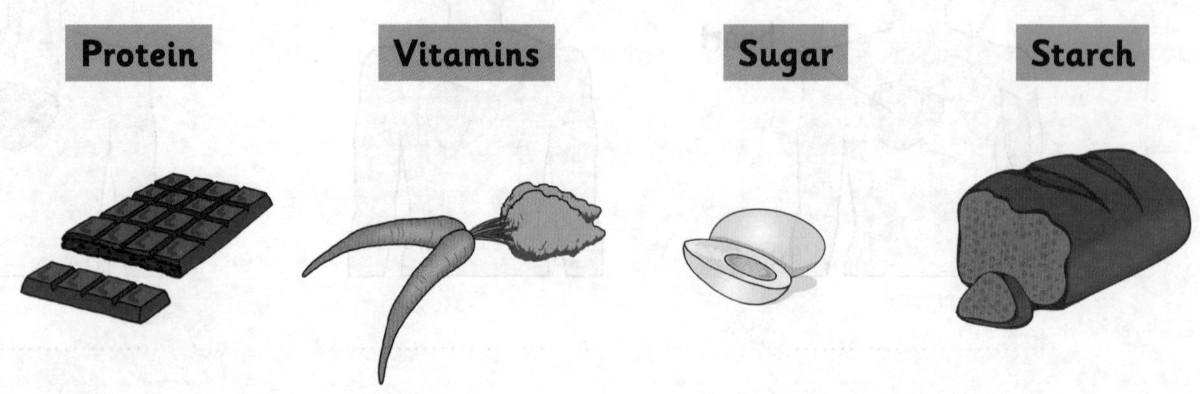

Eating Healthily

4 Kate says: "Eating protein is not important if you eat enough of the other nutrients." Do you agree with Kate? Explain your answer.

....

....

5 Have a look at what Ty eats one day.

Breakfast: orange and a yoghurt

Lunch: tomato soup

Snack: apple and a chocolate bar

Dinner: roast chicken with cauliflower, carrots and peas

Circle the food group that Ty is missing out on.

Protein Fat Fibre

Sugary carbohydrate Starchy carbohydrate

Give an example of something he could eat to get more of this food group.

....

6 Martha predicts that eating pasta the day before going for a run will help her go faster. Over a few weeks, she does three runs without eating pasta the day before, and then does three runs where she does eat pasta the day before. She finds that she runs more quickly for the second group of runs.

Do Martha's results agree with her prediction? Explain why or why not.

....

....

Give a reason why Martha's results might not prove that eating pasta helps her to run faster.

....

....

Now Try This

Look at the packaging of some different types of food. Choose a nutrient (e.g. protein) and compare the amount of that nutrient you get in 100 g of different foods. Does it match what you'd expect based on the type of food?

Exercise

Exercising is key to keeping your body healthy. Plus, it can be pretty fun.

1 **Tick the box next to each sentence about exercise that is true.**

Exercising can make it easier for you to sleep.	☐	You can develop your body's coordination by exercising.	☐
Exercise is bad for your lungs and heart.	☐	Having strong muscles has nothing to do with exercise.	☐

2 **Look at what each person below is doing. Which person do you think will be breathing the most quickly? Explain your answer.**

Ade **John** **Charlotte**

....

....

3 **Alastair wants to see how exercising affects how much he weighs. He eats the same diet for two months. In the first month he exercises as normal, but in the second month he does twice as much exercise.**

What is Alastair doing to help make the test fair?

....

Do you think Alastair will lose weight, stay the same or put weight on? Explain your answer.

....

....

Now Try This **Make a list of different types of exercise you enjoy doing. How do you feel after each one? Which do you think is best for you and why?**

Drugs

Drugs have many health risks. They can be dangerous for your body.

1 **Use the words below to complete the table showing some effects of substances on the body.**

heart	nicotine	liver	sniffing	breathing	stomach
alcohol	lung	damage	reactions	addictive	

Substance	Effect
Tobacco	Tobacco contains .... which is addictive. Smoking can cause .... attacks, ... cancer and .... problems.
....	Drinking alcohol slows your .... down. Drinking lots can damage your heart, ... and ....
Solvents	.... solvents can be .... and can .... your brain.

2 **Read these sentences about alcohol. One word in each sentence is wrong.**

Write down which word is wrong and an example of how to make it right.

Alcohol is a plant found in drinks like wine and beer.

Wrong word: .... New word: ....

Drinking lots of alcohol could reduce your blood pressure.

Wrong word: .... New word: ....

One short-term effect of drinking alcohol is quicker reactions.

Wrong word: .... New word: ....

End of Topic Quiz

Here's a recap on how your body works and how to keep it healthy — enjoy.

1 **Circle two foods that contain lots of fat.**

2 marks

2 **Circle three boxes that describe possible long-term effects of smoking.**

slow reactions	heart attacks	liver failure
brain damage	addiction to nicotine	lung cancer

3 marks

3 **Unscramble the names of the three types of blood vessel, then draw a line to match each one to its description.**

NIVE	....	Where substances leave the blood.
YALIRCLAP	....	Takes blood away from the heart.
RETRAY	....	Takes blood towards the heart.

3 marks

4 **Write numbers in the boxes to put these sentences about transport in the body in the right order. The first one has been done for you.**

- [ ] Blood carries food, water and oxygen to other parts of the body.
- [ ] The blood takes waste substances to the lungs and kidneys.
- [1] The body takes in food, water and oxygen.
- [ ] Different parts of the body use the food and oxygen.

2 marks

End of Topic Quiz

5 **Write down three positive effects that exercise has on the body.**

1. ....
2. ....
3. ....

3 marks

6 **Answer these quick questions about the heart.**

Describe where the heart is within the body.

....

Which part of the body protects the heart?

....

2 marks

7 **Fill in the gaps to complete this table about different food groups.**

Food group	What do you use them for?	Examples of foods that have them
Starchy carbohydrates	....	Bread, ...
.... carbohydrates	Energy	Cakes, sweets
Fats	....	Cheese, ...
....	Growth and	Fish, ...

8 marks

Score: ☐ /**23**

Variation and Inheritance

Living things have lots of differences in their characteristics — this is called variation. Many of a living thing's characteristics are inherited (passed down) from its parents.

1 **Use the clues to complete the crossword. The first letter of each word has been filled in for you.**

Down: 1. A parent's child is its ____________.

2. The term used to describe the differences between living things.

Across: 3. A feature of a living thing.

4. When a feature is passed on from a parent to its child we say the feature has been ____________.

2 **Circle the young rabbit that is most likely to belong to the parents shown.**

Circle the correct words to complete these sentences:

Offspring **are / are not** usually identical to their parents.

Offspring **are / are not** usually identical to each other.

Variation and Inheritance

3 **Look at the parents and their child below.**

Write down one characteristic the boy has inherited from his father.

....

Write down one characteristic the boy has inherited from his mother.

....

Suggest two other characteristics that the child might inherit from his parents. They don't have to be things you can see in the picture.

1. ....

2. ....

4 **The two dogs below are going to have puppies together. Tick the characteristics you think the puppies could inherit, and cross the ones you think they couldn't.**

straight hair ☐

pointy nose ☐

sore leg ☐

bushy tail ☐

ponytail ☐

curly hair ☐

Draw a picture to show what one of the puppies might look like. Label the characteristics you draw.

A Goldendoodle is a type of dog that is created when a Golden Retriever reproduces with a Poodle. Do some research and see if you can find out what characteristics a Goldendoodle inherits from each of its parents.

Adaptations of Animals

Animals have adaptations (special features) that help them survive where they live.

1. **Read the statements about how adaptations affect an animal in its natural habitat. Circle the statements that are true.**

They often make it harder to get enough food.	They often make an animal feel too hot.	They can help an animal move around more easily.
They can help an animal hide from predators.	They make it more likely that the animal will die.	They can help to stop an animal from getting too cold.

2. **Draw lines to match each adaptation to the reason why it's useful.**

Adaptation	**Reason why it's useful**
Fur the same colour as the surroundings	Helps an animal to pick up food
Sharp claws	Helps an animal to feel its surroundings
Whiskers	Helps an animal to stay warm
Thick fur	Helps an animal to sneak up on its prey

3. **Penguins are birds that live in very cold environments. They live on land but dive down into cold water to catch fish to eat. They have large webbed feet.**

Suggest one reason why having large webbed feet could be helpful for a penguin, and one reason why it might not be helpful.

Having large webbed feet could be helpful because ....

....

Having large webbed feet might not be helpful because ....

....

Adaptations of Animals

4 Camels live in hot, sandy deserts.

Circle the correct words in the labels to describe a camel's adaptations.

long / short eyelashes for keeping **water / sand** out of the eyes

not much **fat / water** on the body, meaning it's easier to keep **cool / warm**

brown fur is good for **camouflage / keeping dry**

narrow / wide feet, meaning they don't sink easily into the **sand / snow**

5 Look at the picture of an egret and read the information.

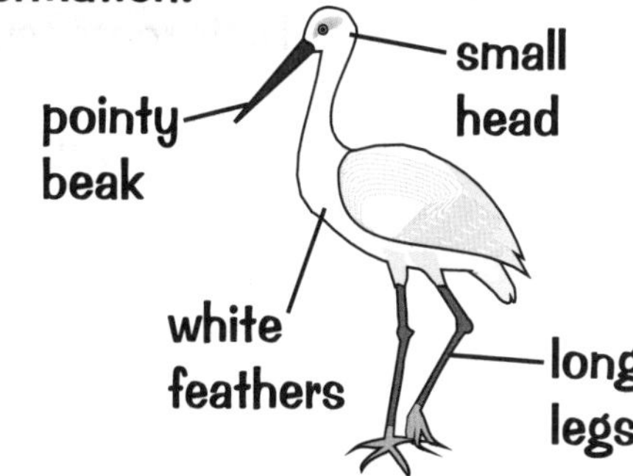

> Egrets often live near the coast. They eat fish, which they can catch by walking across wet sand and into the water where the fish live.

Choose two features labelled on the egret that are adaptations which would help it to survive in its habitat. Write them down and describe why each adaptation is helpful.

Adaptation 1: ....

Reason why it's helpful: ....

....

Adaptation 2: ....

Reason why it's helpful: ....

....

In some animals, the size of their ears is an adaptation. See if you can find pictures of foxes that live in different parts of the world, e.g. the Fennec fox and the Arctic fox. Which has smaller ears? Why do you think this is?

Adaptations of Plants

Just like animals, plants also have adaptations that help them survive.

1 **Choose the correct words from the list below to complete the sentences about cactuses.**

needles wet fat water dry leaves

stems short eating long storing roots

Cactuses are found in very .... places, such as deserts.

They have sharp, thin .... instead of ....

This adaptation stops them from losing too much ....

It also helps to stop animals from .... them.

Their roots tend to be very ...., which helps them to get enough water. They also have thick ...., which are used for .... water.

2 **Look at the picture of a plant.**

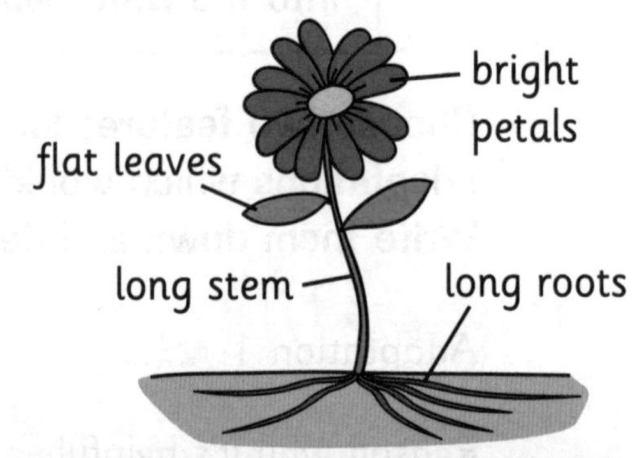

Complete the table to show how the features labelled on the picture help the plant to survive. You can write the same feature more than once, or not at all.

Feature	How it helps
....	Allow lots of minerals and water to be absorbed.
....	Allow lots of light to be absorbed.
....	Attract insects for pollination.
....	Help to stop the plant from getting blown over in the wind.

Fossils

Fossils can tell us what life on Earth might have looked like a long, long time ago.

1. **Circle the correct description of fossils.**

Fossils are the bones of animals that have recently died.	Fossils are living things that have been frozen in ice.	Fossils are the shapes of living things that died a long time ago.

2. **Tick all the statements about fossils that are true.**

Some fossils are millions of years old. ☐

Fossils only show us what animals might have looked like, not plants. ☐

Lots of the fossils that have been found look different from living things that are alive on Earth today. ☐

It is possible to find fossils of all living things that have existed on Earth. ☐

3. **The pictures below show a fossil and an animal that lives on Earth today. A scientist thinks that the animal that made the fossil was related to the animal that's alive on Earth today.**

Fossil

Animal alive today

Describe one difference you can see between the shape of the fossil and the shape of the animal alive on Earth today.

....

....

Suggest one reason why the shapes might be different.

....

....

Fossils

4 **A scientist has found three fossils of the same type of reptile.**

The picture on the right shows which rock layers the three fossils were found in.

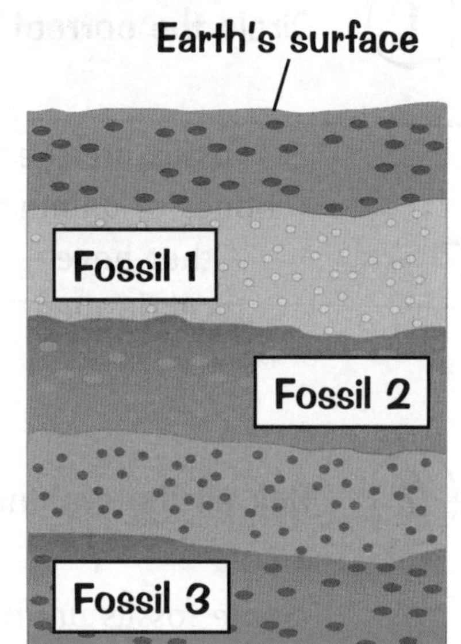

The scientist knows that Fossil 3 is the oldest, and Fossil 1 is the youngest. Use the picture to suggest how she knows this.

....

....

....

....

The scientist lines the fossils up from Fossil 1 to Fossil 3 and compares them. Circle the correct words below to explain why she does this.

By putting the fossils in **age / size** order, the scientist can see how the reptile **evolved / died** .

The scientist measured the size of the head, legs, and body of the fossils she found. Her results are shown in the table below.

Body part	Length (cm)		
	Fossil 1	Fossil 2	Fossil 3
Head	12	12	11
Legs	5	7	9
Body	25	24	25

Underline the sentence that is a good conclusion for the scientist's results.

As time went on, the size of the reptile's legs got shorter.

The reptile's head got shorter over time.

Reptiles that lived long ago had longer bodies than reptiles that lived more recently.

Mary Anning is a famous scientist who discovered many fossils. Do some research and write a fact sheet about her discovery of an ichthyosaur.

Evolution

Evolution describes the change in organisms that happens over a very, very long time.

1 **Tick the sentence about evolution which is false.**

- Evolution makes an animal more suited to its habitat. ☐
- Evolution usually takes place over many years. ☐
- An animal evolves as it grows from a young animal into an adult. ☐

2 **Some plants have thorns and spiky leaves. These characteristics make it difficult for animals to eat the plants without getting hurt.**

Look at the plants on the right. Which do you think is most likely to survive in an area with animals that eat plants? Tick the correct plant.

☐ ☐

Decide whether the statement below is true or false for your chosen plant. Circle the correct answer.

The plant will be more likely to reproduce and pass its features on to its offspring. True / False

3 **Giraffes have very long necks, which allow them to reach leaves on high branches of trees. Eating leaves is important for a giraffe's survival. It's thought that most giraffes had shorter necks many years ago, but over time giraffes evolved to have long necks.**

Explain how giraffes might have evolved to have long necks.

....

....

....

....

....

....

....

End of Topic Quiz

That was a tricky topic — see how much you can remember with this quiz.

1 **Choose the correct words to complete the sentences below about fossils.**

Earth | fossils | millions | evolved | shapes | rocks

Fossils are found in .... They are the .... of living things that lived on .... but died .... of years ago. Scientists are interested in finding .... because they can help us understand how living things .... over time.

3 marks

2 **Circle the correct description of an adaptation.**

Any feature of a living thing that can be inherited by its offspring.	A special feature of a living thing that helps it survive in its habitat.	A special feature of a living thing that makes it different from its parents.

1 mark

3 **Tick the correct boxes to show whether the following statements are true or false.**

	True	False
Offspring usually inherit a mix of characteristics from both parents.	☐	☐
Living things on Earth today may still be evolving.	☐	☐
All types of animals living in the same environment have the same adaptations.	☐	☐

3 marks

End of Topic Quiz

4 **Circle the correct words to complete the sentences about inheritance.**

Offspring / parents inherit some characteristics from their **offspring / parents** .

Offspring are usually **different from / identical to** their parents.

The **similarities / differences** between living things are called **variation / evolution** .

3 marks

5 **Look at the picture of a polar bear.**

Write down two adaptations of polar bears that help them survive in their cold and snowy habitat.

1. ....

2. ....

2 marks

6 **Write numbers in the boxes to put the sentences about evolution in order. The first one has been done for you.**

[1] Some living things have characteristics which make them better suited to their environment. This means they are more likely to survive and reproduce.

[ ] When the offspring reproduce, these characteristics are likely to get passed on again.

[ ] Over time, more and more of the living things in the environment will inherit the characteristics that are good for survival.

[ ] The offspring are likely to inherit some of the characteristics from their parents that make it easier to survive.

2 marks

Score: [ ] **/14**

How We See

You're able to see this page thanks to some important properties of light.

1 **Tick the boxes for the statements that are true.**

Without light, you can't see anything. ☐	Light can bend to travel around corners. ☐
Light travels away from light sources. ☐	When light hits an object, all of it gets absorbed. ☐

2 **Draw two light rays on this picture to show how Rufus the dog is able to see his ball.**

3 **Circle the correct words to complete this paragraph.**

Light travels in **straight / curved** lines. We see things when light **leaves / enters** our eyes. This light can come directly **to / from** a light source or **bounce off / travel around** objects.

4 **Write down two things that are wrong with this diagram showing light rays and a light source.**

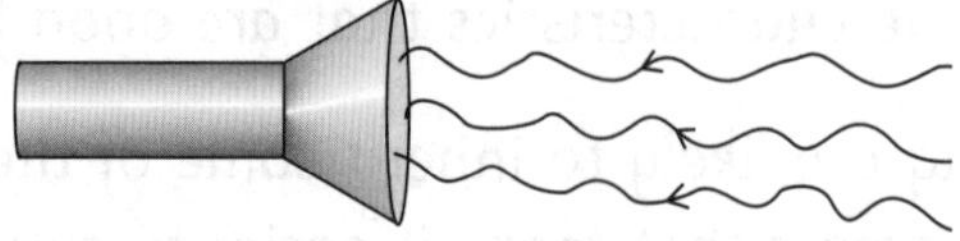

1. ....

2. ....

How We See

5 **Write 'yes' or 'no' to complete the table for each situation.**

	Does it give out light?	Can you see it?
an unlit candle in the light	....	....
a lit candle in the dark	....	....
a lit match in the light	....	....
a flamingo in the dark	....	....

6 **Travis is in a storeroom. He has a torch, which he keeps pointed in the same direction, and there is a light bulb hanging from the ceiling.**

The pink boxes contain different combinations of the things in the room. Write the correct letter next to each sentence below to show which items Travis would be able to see in that situation.

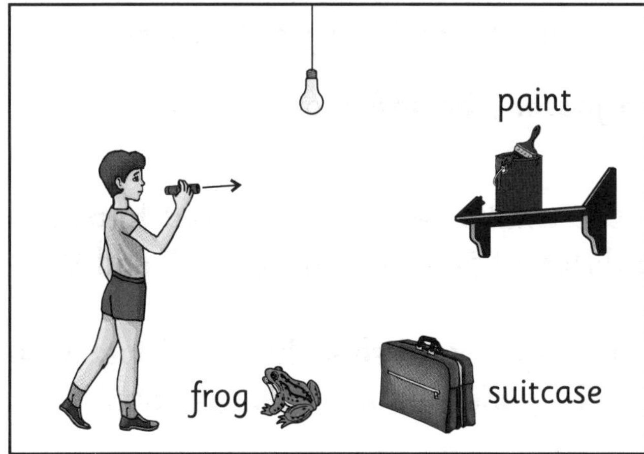

A. suitcase and paint

B. nothing

C. paint

D. suitcase, paint and frog

The torch is turned **on** and the light bulb is turned **off**. ☐

The torch is turned **off** and the light bulb is turned **on**. ☐

The torch is turned **off** and the light bulb is turned **off**. ☐

Look at a safe light source (e.g. a torch) through different coloured sheets of cellophane paper. Write down and compare what you see for each one.

Mirrors and Reflections

Mirrors can be very useful to us because of how they reflect light.

1. **For each diagram, circle the object that the ray being reflected in the mirror will hit.**

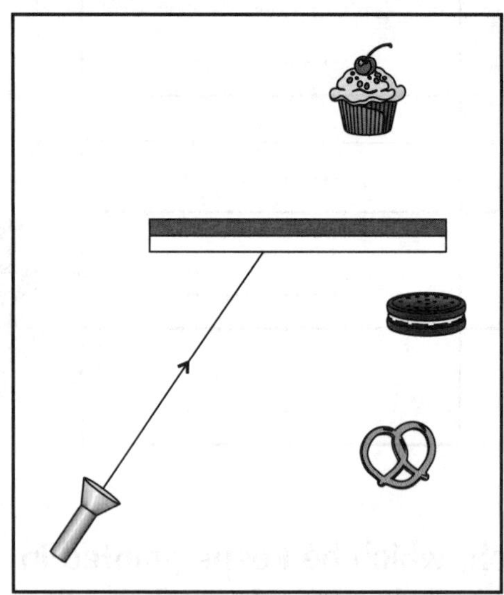

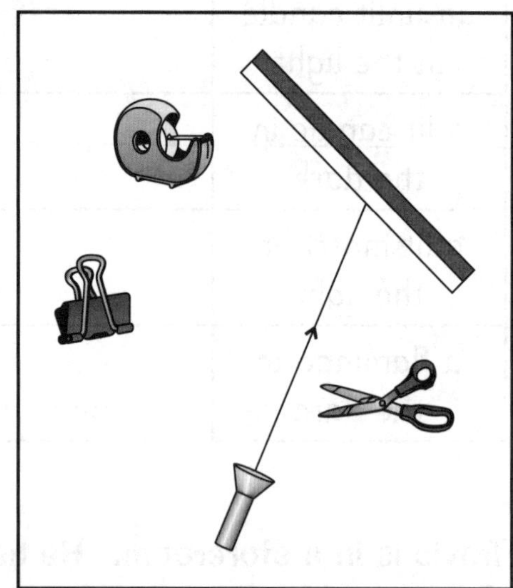

2. **Circle the correct words to complete this paragraph.**

When light reaches a mirror, it **changes direction / goes through** .

Cars have mirrors so the driver can see what's **in front of / behind** them.

This means the driver can **go faster / be safer** on the road.

3. **Mishika wants to be able to see what's behind her without turning around. She has made two different periscope designs, A and B.**

Complete the light rays on the diagrams to show how each periscope will work. Circle the letter of the periscope that Mishika should use.

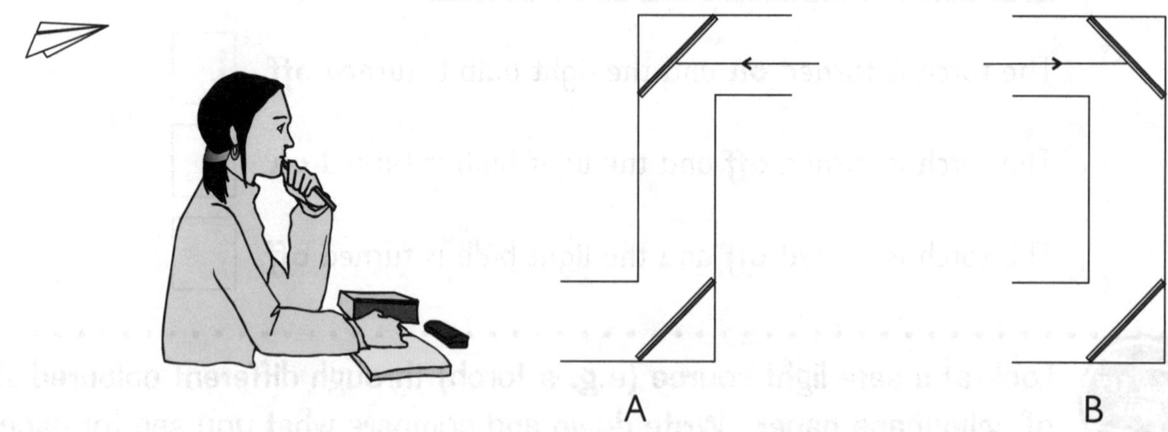

Shadows

What happens if something gets in the way of the light? Introducing: shadows...

1 **Where would a light source need to be to cast the shadow shown? Circle the correct letter.**

A B

C

2 **The diagram shows a stick in the ground and its shadow. The Sun is currently at position A.**

Tick the sentence that is correct.

B

When the Sun is at position B, the shadow will be longer.	☐
When the Sun is at position B, the shadow will be shorter.	☐

3 **Claire makes some statements about shadows.**

Circle the correct word to show whether the statements are true or false.

My shadow will be shortest at midday. True / False

When I cast a shadow, light is passing through me. True / False

My shadow is always a different shape to me. True / False

Shadows

4 Jamilla puts a box in front of a torch.

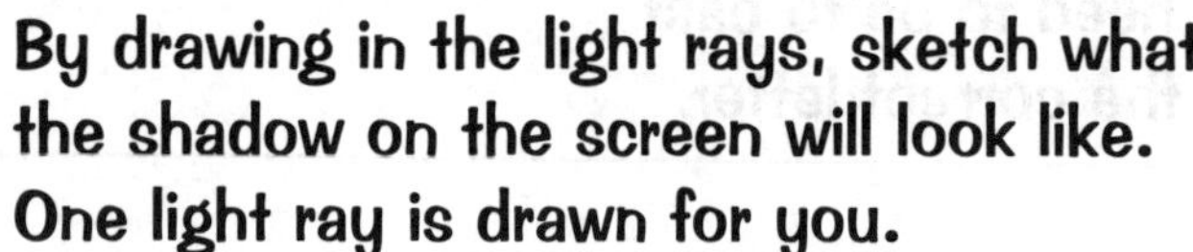

By drawing in the light rays, sketch what the shadow on the screen will look like. One light ray is drawn for you.

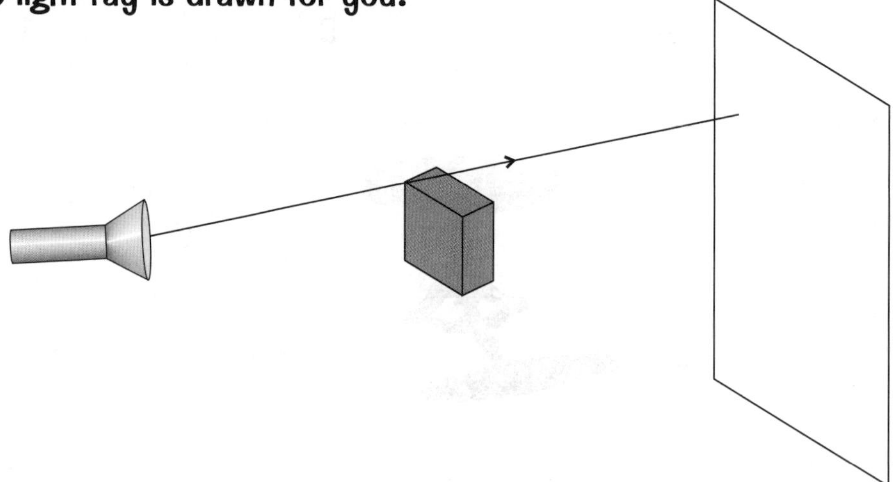

Suggest one way that Jamilla could make the shadow smaller.

....

5 Draw the shadows of the objects below. You could complete the light rays travelling past the edges of the objects to help you.

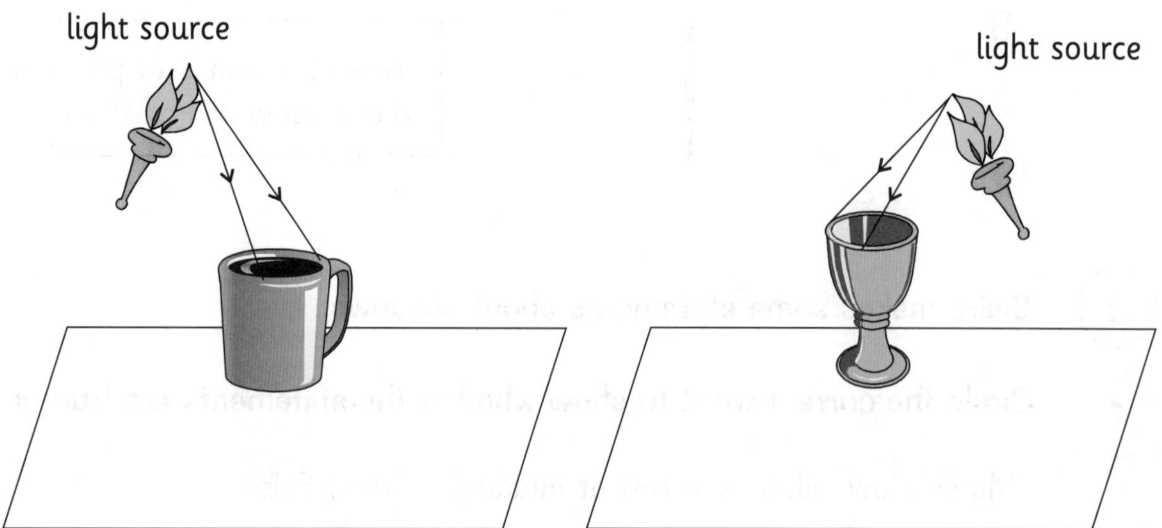

Cut out some interesting shapes from card and hold them in front of a light source to cast shadows on a wall. How do the shadows change as you move the shapes? What about if you move the light source?

End of Topic Quiz

Now that we've shed some light on the topic, it's time for a quiz!

1. Circle the sources of light.

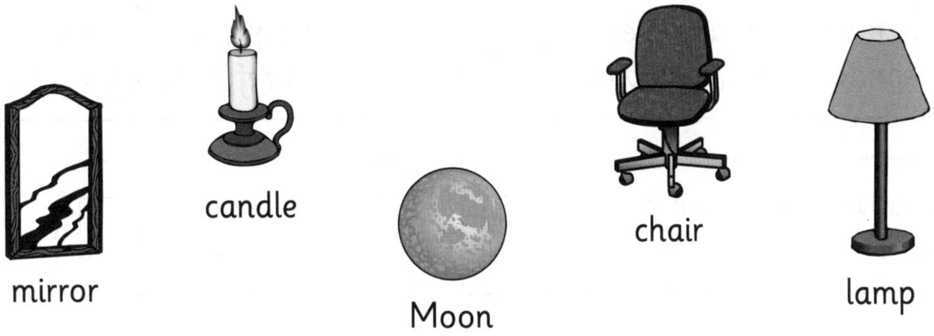

mirror candle Moon chair lamp

2 marks

2. Give an example of how mirrors can be useful.

....

....

1 mark

3. How many arrows correctly show how light could travel from the light source? Write your answer in the box.

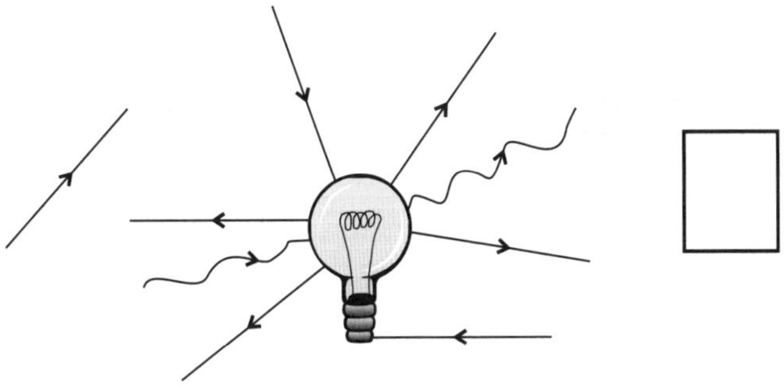

1 mark

4. Write down two things that affect the size of a shadow.

1. ....

2. ....

2 marks

The quiz continues on the next page.

End of Topic Quiz

5 **Tick the boxes for the two statements that are true.**

- If you move a light source closer to an object, its shadow will get smaller. ☐
- We can see things that aren't light sources because light is reflected off them. ☐
- Shadows are caused by the object emitting darkness. ☐
- Light travels in straight lines. ☐

2 marks

6 **What shadow will the cut-out of the letter E make if a lamp is placed in front of it? Circle your answer.**

cut-out

1 mark

7 **Draw the reflected light ray from the mirror in each diagram.**

2 marks

8 **Circle the correct words to complete this paragraph.**

Shadows are caused when light is **magnified / blocked** by an object.

The shadow will be a very **similar / different** shape to the object,

because light travels in **straight / wavy** lines.

3 marks

Score: ☐ **/14**

Circuit Diagrams and Symbols

Circuit symbols allow you to show what's in a circuit, just with less fiddly drawing.

1 **Draw the circuit symbol for each component named below.**

Motor

Cell

Bulb

Buzzer

Switch (off)

2 **Match the symbols to the descriptions of what each component does.**

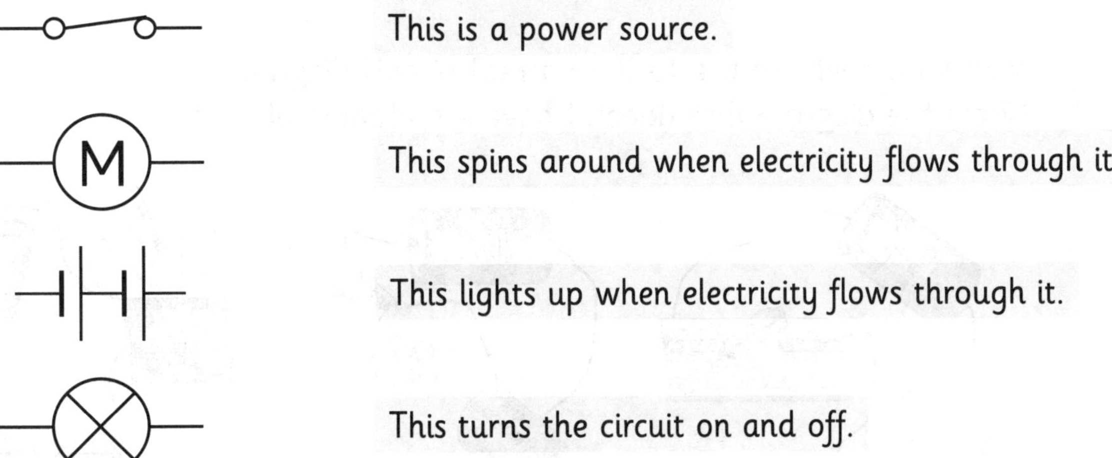

This is a power source.

This spins around when electricity flows through it.

This lights up when electricity flows through it.

This turns the circuit on and off.

3 **Draw a circuit diagram for a complete circuit with two cells, a bulb, a buzzer, and a switch.**

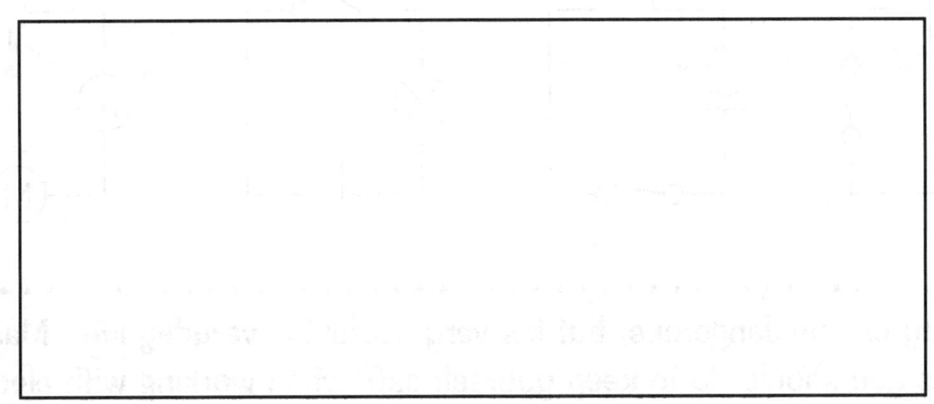

Circuit Diagrams and Symbols

4 Brenda wants to make a circuit that includes a bulb which is lit up. Which of these circuit diagrams could she use to make her circuit? Tick the box next to each one that is suitable.

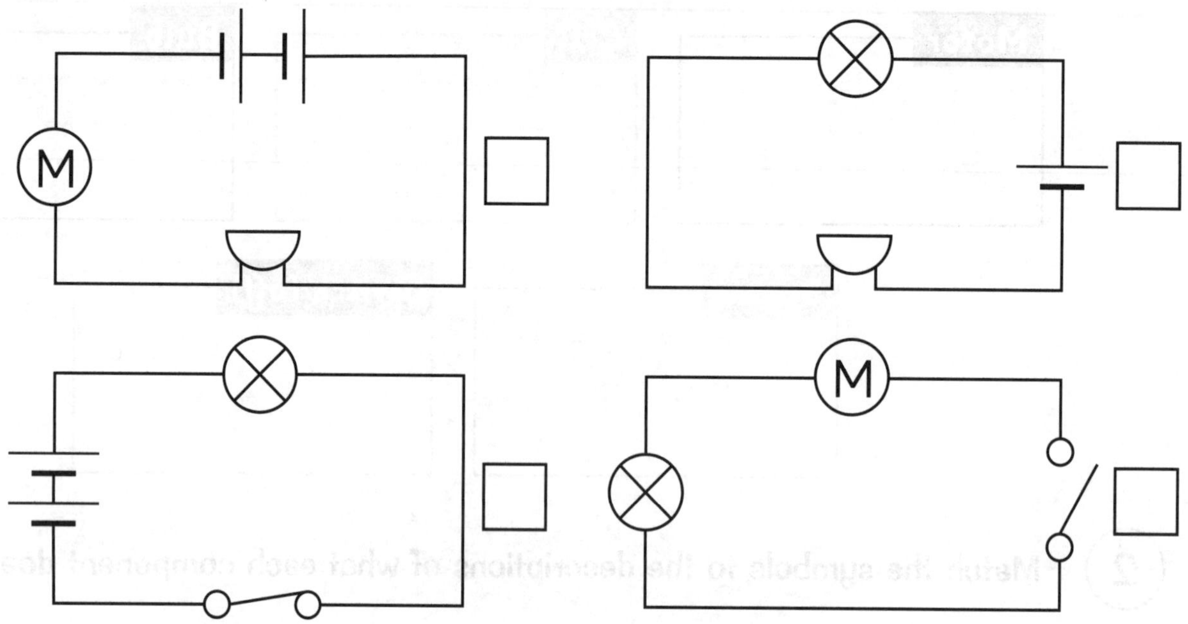

5 Match up each picture to the correct circuit diagram. Circle the diagram that doesn't have a matching picture.

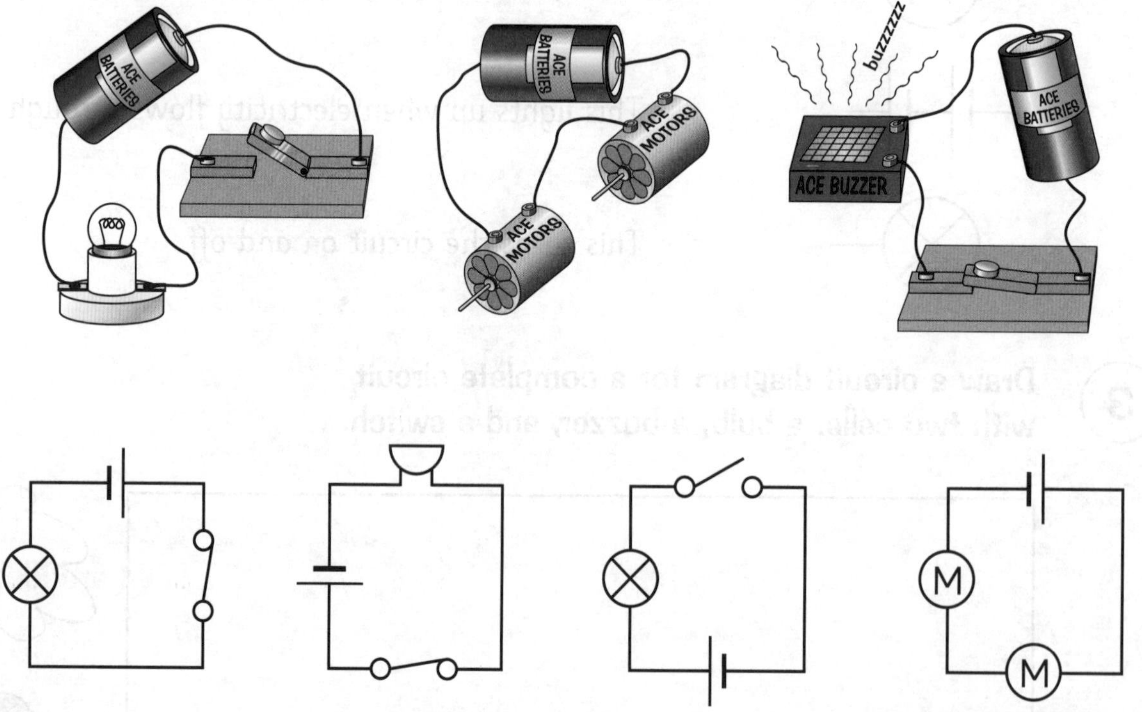

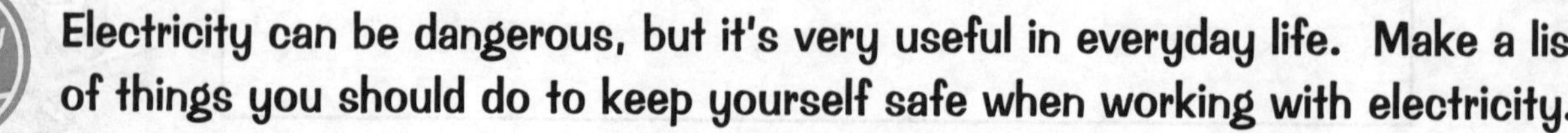

Now Try This Electricity can be dangerous, but it's very useful in everyday life. Make a list of things you should do to keep yourself safe when working with electricity.

Changing Circuits

You can find out more about how circuits work by taking one and changing it slightly.

1 **Carla connects a motor in two different circuits. Which circuit will the motor spin faster in? Tick the correct box.**

A complete circuit with a cell that has a voltage of 1.2 V. ☐	A complete circuit with a cell that has a voltage of 3 V. ☐

2 **Unscramble the words in capitals to fill in the gaps in the sentences below.**

When you add a (MENOCNOPT) .... to a circuit it changes the circuit. If you have a circuit containing one buzzer, adding another buzzer will make each buzzer (ETUERIQ) .... This is because each component gets less (OPREW) .... from the (YARTTEB) ....

3 **Ray wants to change the circuit on the right. He switches the circuit off and connects another cell in between the cell and the switch.**

Ray then switches the circuit back on. Predict what Ray will observe when he does this, compared to the old circuit.

....

Explain why you made this prediction.

....

....

4 **Write in the boxes to rank the brightness of the bulbs in these circuits from 1 (dimmest) to 4 (brightest). The cells and bulbs used are identical.**

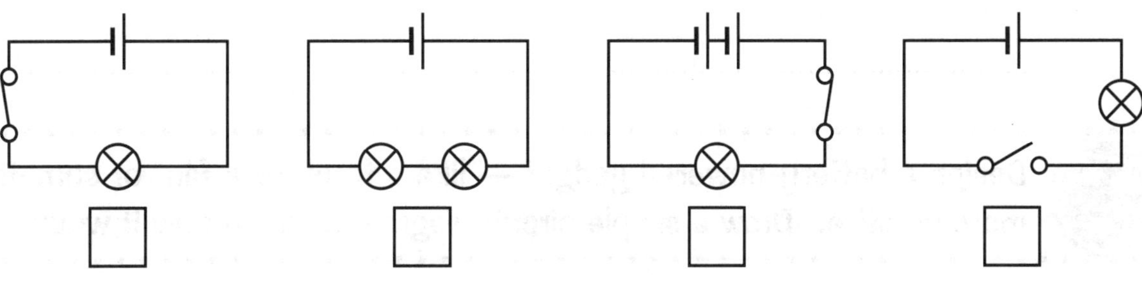

Changing Circuits

5 **Compare each circuit below to the one on the right. State whether the motor will spin faster or slower in each circuit and give a reason why.**

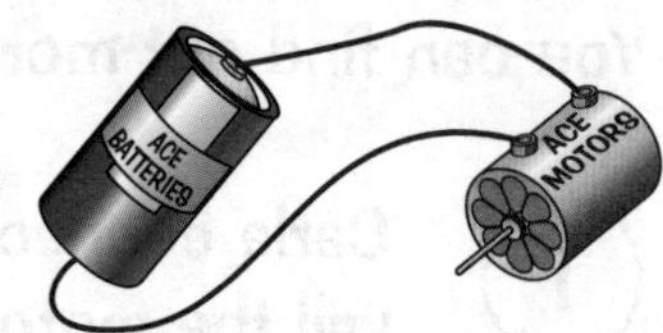

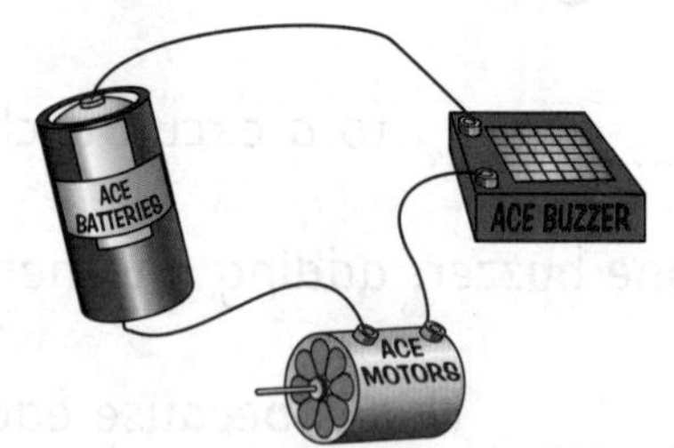

The motor will spin .... in this circuit

because ....

....

The motor will spin .... in this circuit

because ....

....

6 **Aisha wants to make a battery-powered light for reading at night time.**

Add one component to complete this circuit so it would be useful to Aisha.

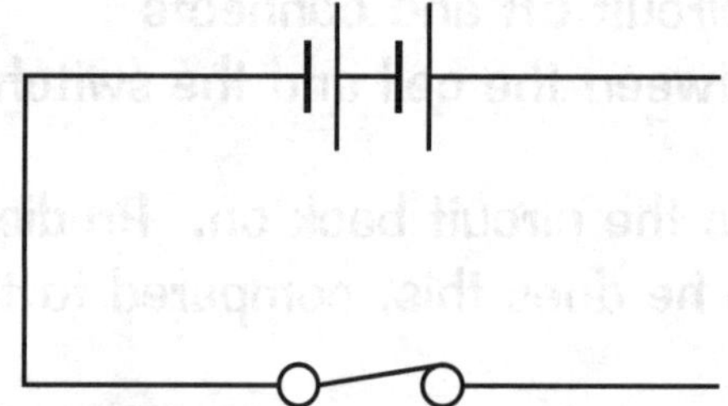

Aisha tests out her reading light, but she finds that it's too bright. Give two ways that she could change her circuit to fix this problem.

1. ....

2. ....

Aisha accidentally changes a cell in her circuit for a cell that is much more powerful. Afterwards she is unable to get her light to work again. Why do you think this happened?

....

Now Try This

Design a battery-powered gadget — like a torch or a fan, or something more creative. Draw a simple circuit diagram to show how it would work.

End of Topic Quiz

That's it for Topic 5 — use this quick quiz to test your knowledge of circuits.

1 **Draw lines to match each circuit symbol to the name of the component.**

M

buzzer switch cell motor bulb

4 marks

2 **Eric makes a complete circuit containing a cell and a bulb. Complete the sentences to describe what happens when he changes the circuit.**

The higher the voltage of the cell, the .... the bulb will be.

Adding more .... to the circuit makes the bulb brighter.

Adding more bulbs to the circuit makes each bulb ....

3 marks

3 **Tick the box next to each of the two options that would make the buzzer in this circuit louder.**

- ☐ Add another cell to the circuit.
- ☐ Open the switch in the circuit.
- ☐ Add a second buzzer to the circuit.
- ☐ Change a cell for one with a higher voltage.
- ☐ Change a cell for one with a lower voltage.
- ☐ Take out one of the cells.

2 marks

Score: ☐ /9

End of Year Test

This test brings together everything you need to know for Year 6 — it's a big one...

1 **Circle the correct words to complete each sentence.**

Your blood absorbs nutrients and water through the **gut / lungs** .

Your **lungs / kidneys** remove waste food products from your blood.

When blood passes through your lungs, it absorbs oxygen from the **air / water** and gets rid of waste **food products / carbon dioxide** .

4 marks

2 **Tick the circuit in which the buzzer will be louder. Explain why you chose that circuit.**

☐

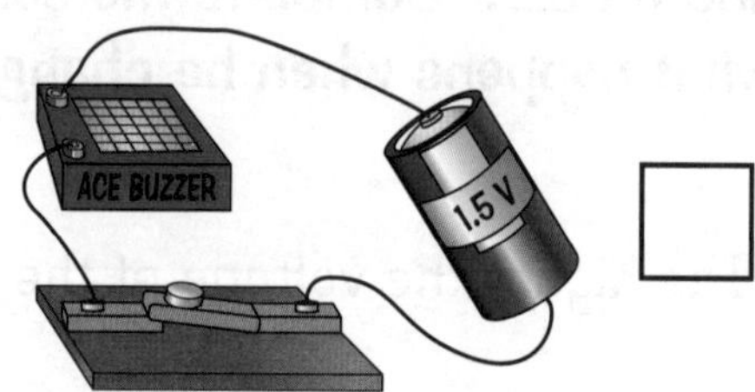

☐

....

....

2 marks

3 **Fill in the missing letters to complete these sentences about staying healthy.**

Drinking too much .... L .... OH .... is bad for your L........ ER , ... EA .... and stomach.	Humans need to eat a B .... LA .... ED diet to get the right amount of different .... UT .... I .... NT .... .

E .... E .... I .... E is important because it S .... RE .... G .... H .... S your muscles and helps to develop your .... U .... GS .

3 marks

End of Year Test

4 **Blood vessels carry blood between different organs of the body.**

Use the words below to fill in the missing labels on the diagram.

vein lung heart capillaries

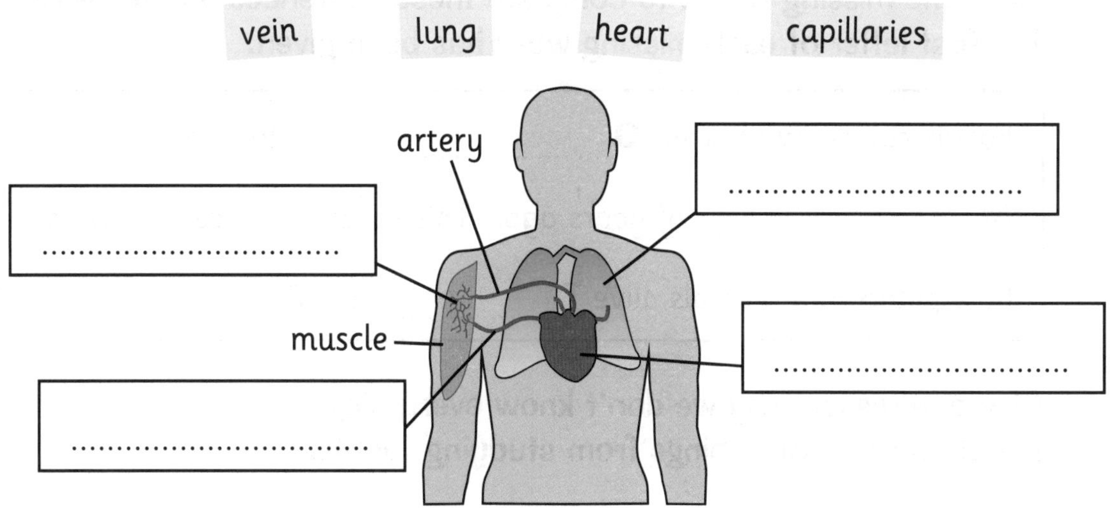

Describe the function of the heart.

....

5 marks

5 **This classification tree shows one way that living things can be split up into different groups. Fill in the boxes to complete the tree.**

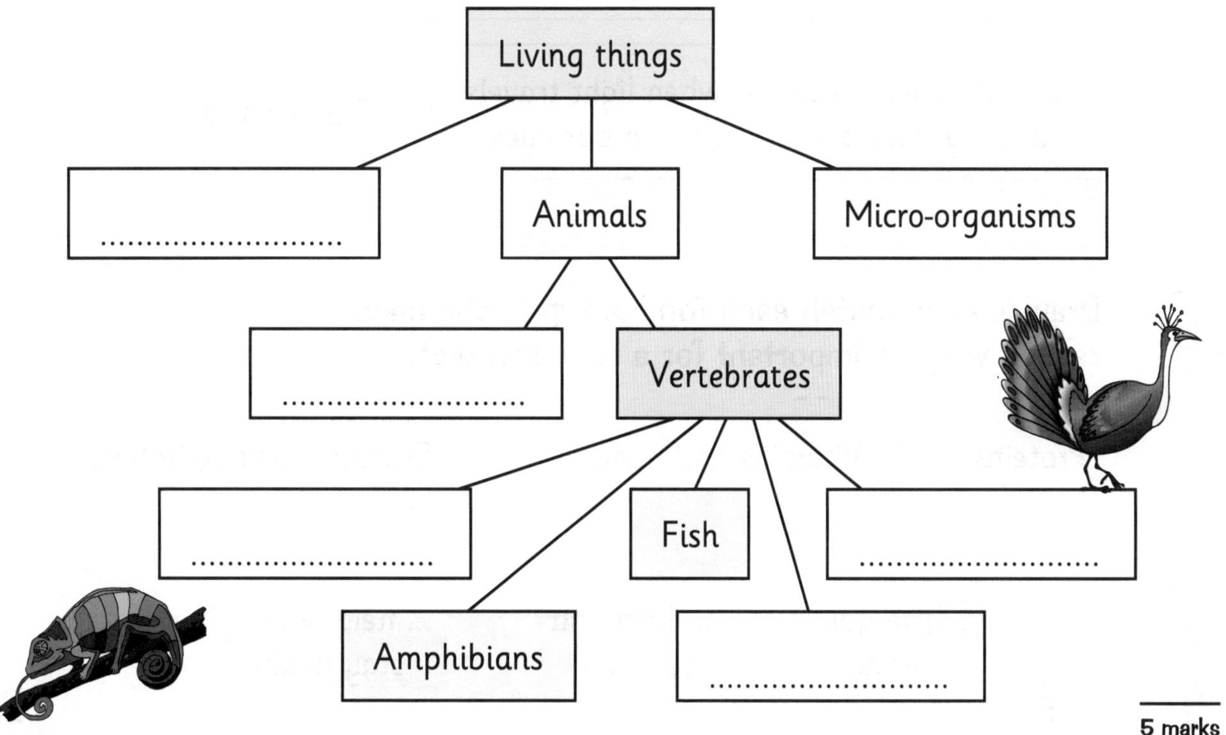

5 marks

End of Year Test

6 **Fossils are the shapes of living things that are made when their remains are trapped in layers of rock.**

Fill in the missing words to complete these sentences about fossils. The first letter of each missing word has been given.

Fossils can show us what **O** .... looked like **M** .... of years ago. This means they can show us how plants and animals alive **T** .... have **E** ....

Give one reason why we don't know everything about ancient living things from studying fossils.

....

3 marks

7 **Circle the right word to show whether each statement is true or false.**

Statement	
Light always travels in a straight line.	True / False
Light reflects well when a surface is shiny.	True / False
We can only see things when light travels directly from a light source to our eyes.	True / False

3 marks

8 **Draw lines to match each food group to the main reason why it's important for a balanced diet.**

Proteins... Vitamins and minerals... Starchy carbohydrates...

... give you energy. ... help you to grow. ... help your cells stay healthy.

2 marks

End of Year Test

9 **Alex is able to see his friend Samantha passing by, even though she is behind him. Draw light rays on the diagram to show how this is possible.**

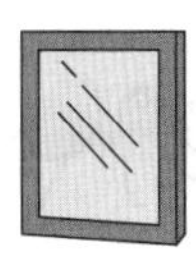

2 marks

10 **Dolphins are mammals that live in the sea. They have a powerful tail for swimming and bony flippers that help them to change direction.**

What word describes a feature of an animal that helps it survive in its habitat? Circle the correct answer.

adaptation   evolution

Suggest a reason why a dolphin's tail and flippers help it to survive.

....

Scientists believe that dolphins evolved from land animals with legs. Circle the correct words to complete the description of how this could have happened.

When the dolphin-like animals started to swim to look for food, those animals with wider, flatter legs were likely to be **better / worse** at swimming, so were more likely to survive and **reproduce / die** . Their offspring were likely to have **evolved / inherited** their parents' wide, flat legs, and so were also more likely to survive. Over time, a **large / small** number of the animals would have had legs like flippers that helped survival.

4 marks

End of Year Test

11 **Look at the four animals below. They are all invertebrates.**

Circle the animal that belongs in a different group to the other three.

Which group of invertebrates do the other three animals belong to?

....

Give two features that are shared by the group of invertebrates you wrote above.

1. ....

2. ....

4 marks

12 **Use the circuit symbols to name the components. Then fill in the gaps to complete the description of each component.**

Name:	Opening and .... this component .... the flow of electricity.
Name:	This component makes a .... when electricity .... through it.

4 marks

13 **Look at the picture of the sandcastle.**

Explain why the sandcastle has a shadow, and why it is the same shape as the sandcastle.

....

....

....

....

2 marks

End of Year Test

14 **Unscramble each word in brackets to fill in the gaps in these sentences.**

The (TFUREASE) .... of a living thing are its characteristics. Some characteristics are (DIRHEINET) ...., which means they are passed from parents to (FNIRPOFGS) .... Living things that are closely related share lots of characteristics but they are not (ACLITINED) .... — the differences between them are called (ARANOVITI) ....

5 marks

15 **Jason is building a simple circuit to make a lamp for his bedroom.**

He makes a circuit that has a cell, a bulb and a switch.
Using circuit symbols, draw a diagram to show this circuit with the bulb lit.

Jason swaps the 3 V cell he used in the first circuit for a 1.5 V cell.
How will this affect the bulb when the circuit is switched on?
Explain your answer.

....

....

....

4 marks

Score: ☐ **/52**

Answers

Topic 1 – Living Things and Their Habitats

Pages 2-3 – Grouping Organisms

1.

Vertebrate Invertebrate

snail eagle frog crab shark

2.

	Found in ponds and lakes	Grows several metres high
Flowering	water lily	oak tree
Non-flowering	algae	pine tree

3. Same: E.g. both animals have wings. / Both animals have legs.
Different: E.g. the bird has 2 legs but the bee has 6 legs. / The bird has a beak. / The bee has antennae.
4. No, because Prakash's micro-organism belongs in group B and the micro-organisms in group B are harmless.
5. Insect, Bird, Reptile

Pages 4-5 – Classification Keys

1. carp, zebra, sloth, dove
2.

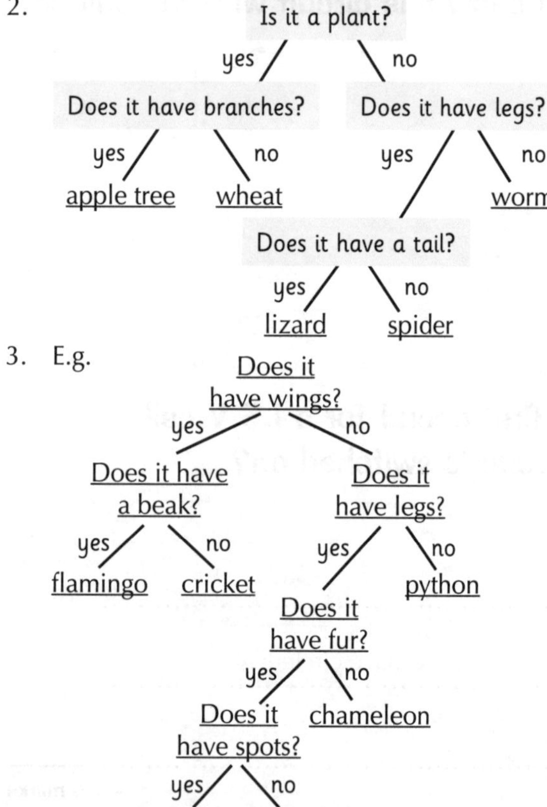

Page 6 – End of Topic Quiz

1. Animals, Plants, Micro-organisms *(1 mark for each correct answer)*
2. An invertebrate is an animal without a backbone. *(1 mark)*
e.g. a snail *(1 mark)*
3. Tigers are vertebrate animals with four legs.
Flowering plants include grasses, cereals and deciduous trees.
Micro-organisms can be split into the groups of bacteria, fungi and viruses.
Non-flowering plants include moss and coniferous trees. *(1 mark for each correct answer)*
4. You should have ticked:
Keys are used to identify unknown organisms.
A key is a series of questions with yes/no answers.
(1 mark for each correct answer)

Topic 2 – Animals Including Humans

Page 7 – The Human Body

1.

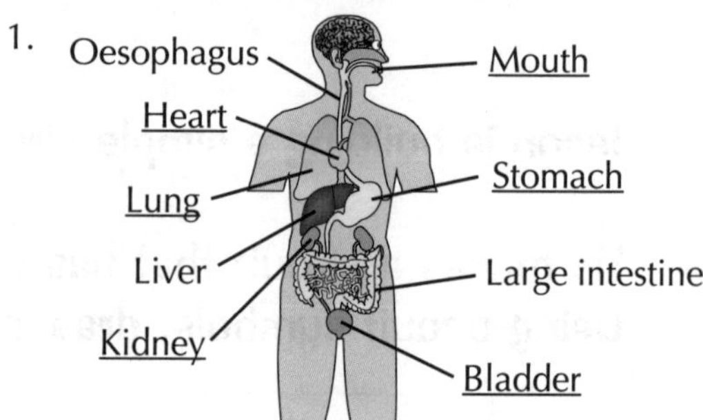

2.

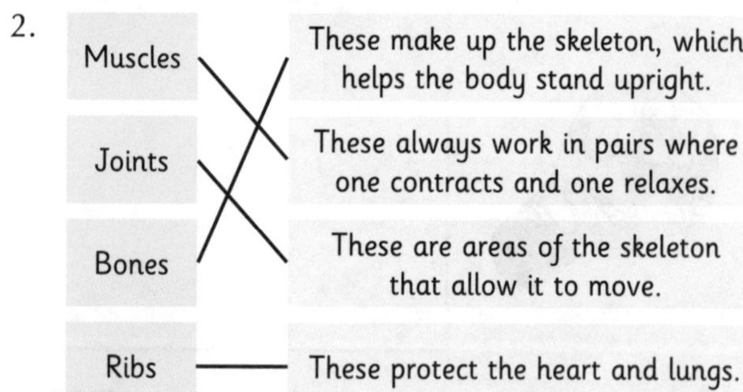

Page 8 – Transport in the Body

1. F, F, T
2. When you eat and drink, your body takes in food and water. These substances get into your blood, which carries them to the rest of the body. Your body uses food to get energy and to help you grow. Your blood also carries waste back to your lungs and kidneys. The kidneys help to get rid of waste food products and water.
3. The lungs take in oxygen, and get rid of waste carbon dioxide.

Answers

Page 9 – Circulation

1. You should have circled:
   blood, heart, blood vessels
2. Any four from: e.g. food / water / oxygen / carbon dioxide / waste products
3. One job of the blood is to DELIVER food and OXYGEN to different parts of the body. The ORGANS of the body all have important functions and they need ENERGY to be able to work properly. Our bodies get ENERGY by using up FOOD and OXYGEN — this means our organs all need BLOOD to provide these ingredients so they keep WORKING.
   All organs have blood vessels because all organs need blood to keep working, and blood travels through blood vessels.

Page 10 – The Heart

1.

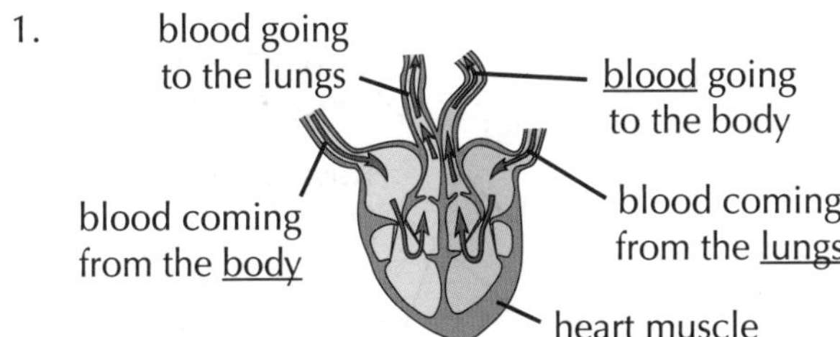

2. Most of the heart is made up of muscle, which allows it to act like a pump.
   When the muscles in the heart contract, they squeeze blood out of the heart.
3. He can feel blood moving through blood vessels near the surface of his skin each time his heart beats.

Page 11 – Blood and Blood Vessels

1. arteries, capillaries, veins
2. The boxes should go 1, 4, 3, 2.
3.

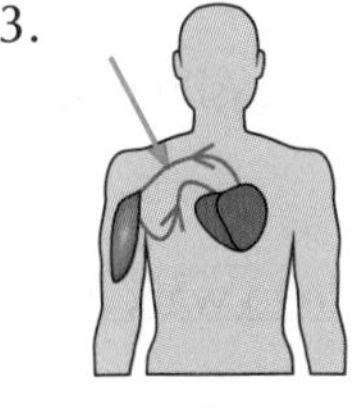
artery

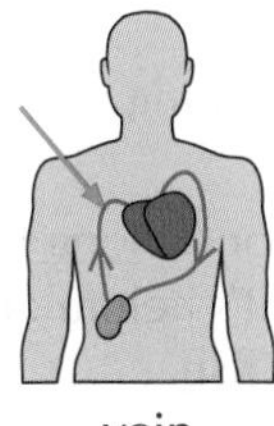
vein

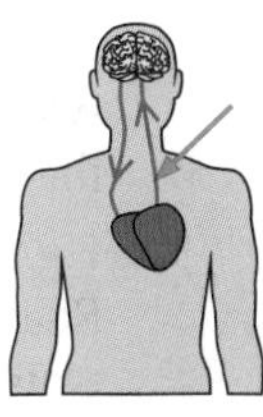
artery

Pages 12-13 – Eating Healthily

1. You should have ticked:

2. The false sentence is:
   It doesn't matter what you eat, as long as it's not too much food.
   This is false because you need to get the right amount of nutrients, so it does matter what you eat.

3.

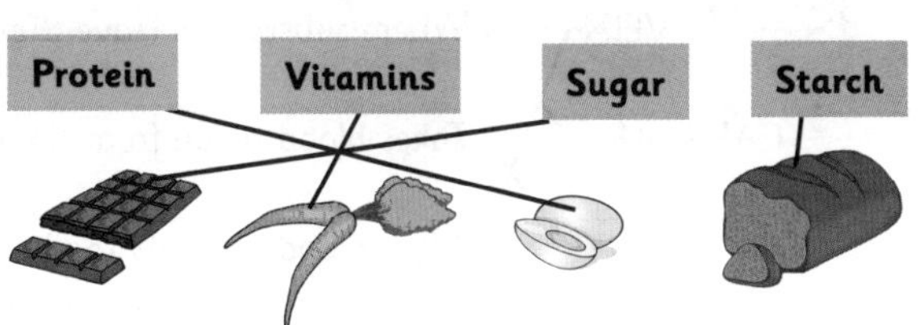

4. No, because proteins are needed for growth and repair.
5. You should have circled: starchy carbohydrate
   E.g. bread / pasta / cereal
6. Yes, as she ran more quickly when she had eaten pasta than when she had not eaten pasta.
   E.g. there could be other things affecting how fast she ran, such as what shoes she wore / how tired she was / what else she had to eat and drink.

Page 14 – Exercise

1. You should have ticked:
   Exercising can make it easier for you to sleep.
   You can develop your body's coordination by exercising.
2. Charlotte, because she is using the most energy, so she'll need to breathe more.
3. He made sure to keep his diet the same.
   E.g. he will lose weight, as he will need more energy so won't store up as much fat.

Page 15 – Drugs

1.

Substance	Effect
Tobacco	Tobacco contains nicotine which is addictive. Smoking can cause heart attacks, lung cancer and breathing problems.
Alcohol	Drinking alcohol slows your reactions down. Drinking lots can damage your heart, liver and stomach.
Solvents	Sniffing solvents can be addictive and can damage your brain.

2. Wrong word: plant — New word: drug
   Wrong word: reduce — New word: increase
   Wrong word: quicker — New word: slower

Pages 16-17 – End of Topic Quiz

1. You should have circled:

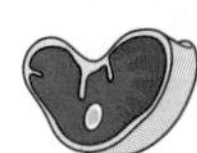 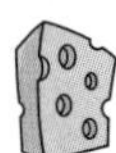

(1 mark for each correct answer)

2. You should have circled:
   heart attacks, addiction to nicotine, lung cancer
   (1 mark for each correct answer)

Answers

3.

VEIN	Where substances leave the blood.
CAPILLARY	Takes blood away from the heart.
ARTERY	Takes blood towards the heart.

(1 mark for each word correctly unscrambled and matched to the correct sentence)

4. The boxes should go 2, 4, 1, 3.
   (2 marks for the correct order, otherwise 1 mark if at least one box is numbered correctly)
5. Any three from: E.g. exercise strengthens muscles like the heart. / Exercise helps develop the lungs. / Exercise helps develop body coordination. / Exercise uses up energy, which helps to stop you becoming overweight. / Exercise can help you sleep well. *(1 mark for each correct answer)*
6. Your heart is in (the middle of) your chest *(1 mark)*.
   the ribs / rib cage *(1 mark)*
7.

Food group	What do you use them for?	Examples of foods that have them
Starchy carbohydrates	Energy	Bread, e.g. pasta / cereals
Sugary carbohydrates	Energy	Cakes, sweets
Fats	Energy	Cheese, e.g. meat / butter / milk
Proteins	Growth and repair	Fish, e.g. milk / meat / eggs

(1 mark for each correct answer)

Topic 3 – Evolution and Inheritance

Pages 18-19 – Variation and Inheritance

1.

1 OFFSPRING
2 VARIATION
3 CHARACTERISTIC
4 INHERITED

2. You should have circled: 

   Offspring are not usually identical to their parents.
   Offspring are not usually identical to each other.

3. e.g. blond hair
   e.g. brown eyes
   e.g. skin colour, height
4. You should have ticked: pointy nose, straight hair, bushy tail, curly hair
   You should have crossed: sore leg, pony tail
   You should have drawn a picture of a dog with some of the characteristics you ticked. Your drawing should be labelled with each of the characteristics you included.

Pages 20-21 – Adaptations of Animals

1. You should have circled:
   They can help an animal hide from predators.
   They can help an animal move around more easily.
   They can help to stop an animal from getting too cold.
2.

Fur the same colour as the surroundings	Helps an animal to pick up food
Sharp claws	Helps an animal to feel its surroundings
Whiskers	Helps an animal to stay warm
Thick fur	Helps an animal to sneak up on its prey

3. E.g. Having large webbed feet could be helpful because it will help the penguin to swim when catching fish to eat.
   E.g. Having large webbed feet might not be helpful because it might make it more difficult for the penguin to move around on land.
4. long eyelashes for keeping sand out of the eyes
   brown fur is good for camouflage
   not much fat on the body, meaning it's easier to keep cool
   wide feet, meaning they don't sink easily into the sand
5. E.g. Adaptation 1: long legs
   Reason why it's helpful: to be able to walk into water to find fish.
   Adaptation 2: pointy beak
   Reason why it's helpful: to be able to catch fish in the water.

Page 22 – Adaptations of Plants

1. Cactuses are found in very dry places, such as deserts. They have sharp, thin needles instead of leaves. This adaptation stops them from losing too much water. It also helps to stop animals from eating them. Their roots tend to be very long, which helps them to get enough water. They also have thick stems, which are used for storing water.

Answers

2.

Feature	How it helps
long roots	Allow lots of minerals and water to be absorbed.
flat leaves	Allow lots of light to be absorbed.
bright petals	Attract insects for pollination.
long roots	Help to stop the plant from getting blown over in the wind.

Pages 23-24 – Fossils

1. You should have circled: Fossils are the shapes of living things that died a long time ago.
2. You should have ticked:
   Some fossils are millions of years old.
   Lots of the fossils that have been found look different from living things that are alive on Earth today.
3. E.g. the animal alive today has longer legs than the animal that made the fossil. / The animal alive today has antennae, unlike the animal that made the fossil. / The animal alive today has a more rounded body shape than the animal that made the fossil.
   E.g. the animal might have evolved over time to have a different shape. / The animal that made the fossil might have been damaged before the fossil formed.
4. The deeper the fossil is buried, the older it is. Fossil 3 is the buried the deepest so it is the oldest and Fossil 1 is buried the least deep so it is the youngest.
   By putting the fossils in age order, the scientist can see how the reptile evolved.
   You should have underlined: As time went on, the size of the reptile's legs got shorter.

Page 25 – Evolution

1. You should have ticked: An animal evolves as it grows from a young animal into an adult.
2. You should have ticked:

   You should have circled: True
3. E.g. the giraffes with the longest necks would have been able to reach leaves from more of the branches, so would have been more likely to survive and reproduce. Some of their offspring would have inherited the longer necks and they also would have been more likely to survive and reproduce. This would have continued over time, until giraffes had evolved to have longer necks.

Pages 26-27 – End of Topic Quiz

1. Fossils are found in rocks. They are the shapes of living things that lived on Earth but died millions of years ago. Scientists are interested in finding fossils because they can help us understand how living things evolved over time. *(3 marks for all 6 answers correct, 2 marks for at least 4 answers correct, or 1 mark for at least 2 answers correct.)*
2. You should have circled: A special feature of a living thing that helps it survive in its habitat. *(1 mark)*
3. You should have ticked: True, True, False *(1 mark for each correct answer)*
4. Offspring inherit some characteristics from their parents. *(1 mark)*
   Offspring are usually different from their parents. *(1 mark)*
   The differences between living things are called variation. *(1 mark)*
5. Any two from: e.g. a round body shape / fat on its body / thick fur / white fur / small ears / a small nose / wide feet *(1 mark for each correct answer)*
6. The boxes should go 1, 3, 4, 2. *(2 marks for all boxes filled in correctly, otherwise 1 mark for at least one box filled in correctly.)*

Topic 4 – Light

Pages 28-29 – How We See

1. You should have ticked:
   Without light, you can't see anything.
   Light travels away from light sources.
2. E.g.

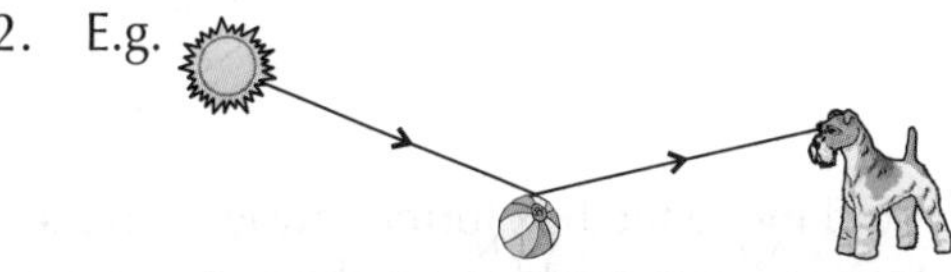

3. Light travels in straight lines. We see things when light enters our eyes. This light can come directly from a light source or bounce off objects.
4. The lines should be straight, not wavy.
   The arrows on the lines should be pointing away from the light source.

Answers

5.

	Does it give out light?	Can you see it?
an unlit candle in the light	no	yes
a lit candle in the dark	yes	yes
a lit match in the light	yes	yes
a flamingo in the dark	no	no

6. C, D, B

Page 30 – Mirrors and Reflections

1.

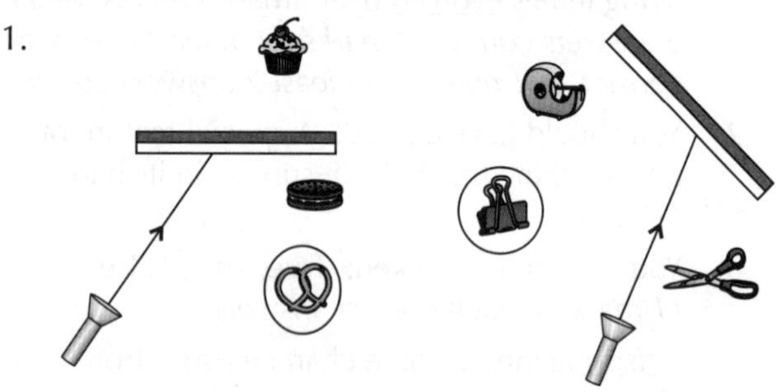

2. When light reaches a mirror, it changes direction. Cars have mirrors so the driver can see what's behind them. This means the driver can be safer on the road.
3. You should have circled: B

Pages 31-32 – Shadows

1. You should have circled: B
2. You should have ticked:
   When the Sun is at position B,
   the shadow will be longer.
3. You should have circled: True, False, False
4.

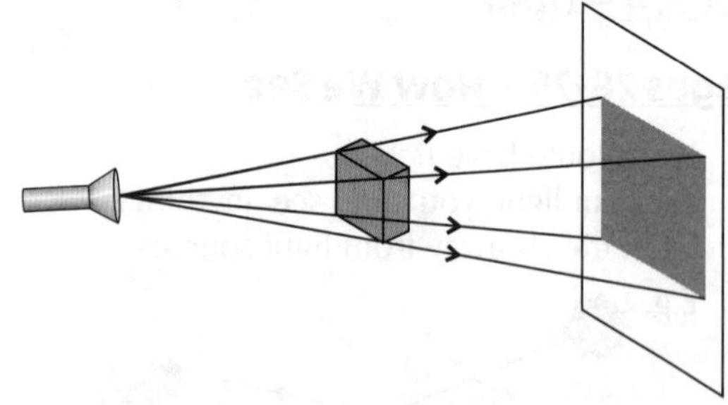

She could move the box further away from the light source. / She could move the light source further away from the box.

5.

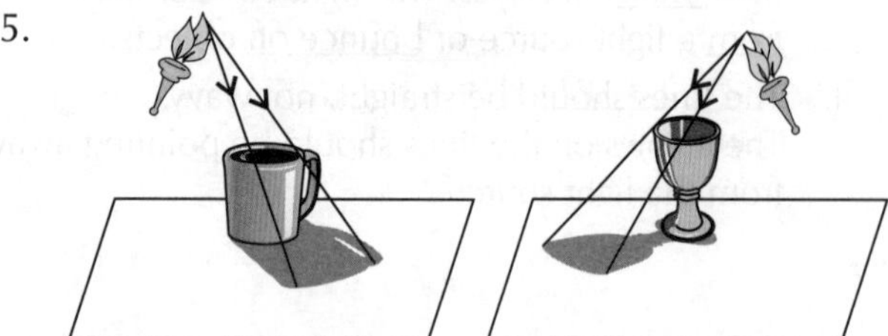

Pages 33-34 – End of Topic Quiz

1. You should have circled: candle, lamp
   (1 mark for each correct answer)
2. E.g. A dentist might use mirrors to see inside someone's mouth and behind their teeth. / You would use a mirror to check your appearance.
   (1 mark)
3. 4 *(1 mark)*
4. Any two from: e.g. the size of the object / the distance from the object to the shadow / the distance from the object to the light source
   (1 mark for each correct answer)
5. You should have ticked:
   We can see things that aren't light sources because light is reflected off them.
   Light travels in straight lines.
   (1 mark for each correct answer)
6. You should have circled:

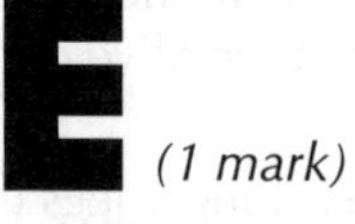

(1 mark)

7.

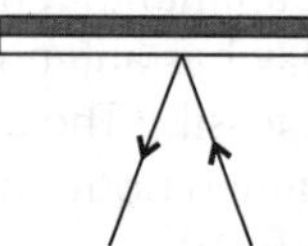

(1 mark for each light ray drawn correctly)

8. Shadows are caused when light is blocked by an object. The shadow will be a similar shape to the object, because light travels in straight lines.
   (1 mark for each correct answer)

Topic 5 – Electricity

Pages 35-36 – Circuit Diagrams and Symbols

1.

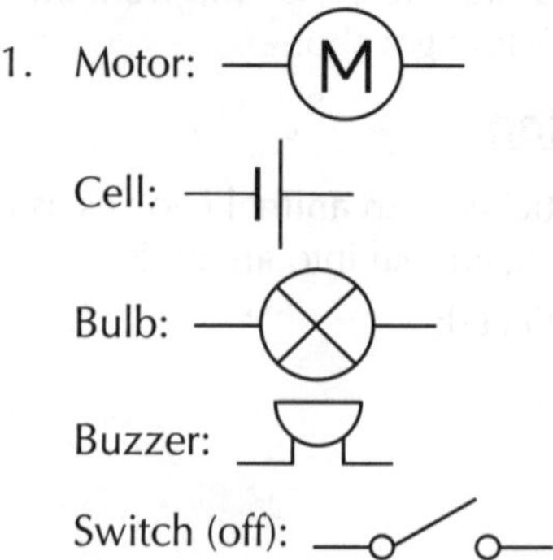

Answers

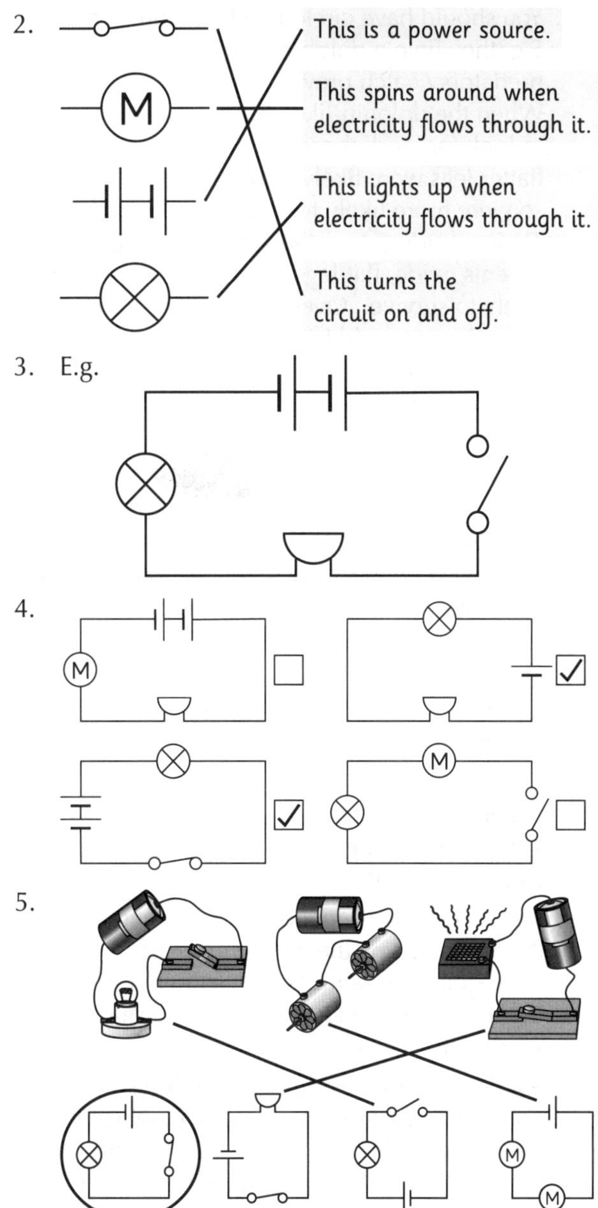

Pages 37-38 – Changing Circuits

1. You should have ticked: A complete circuit with a cell that has a voltage of 3 V.
2. When you add a component to a circuit it changes the circuit. If you have a circuit containing one buzzer, adding another buzzer will make each buzzer quieter. This is because each component gets less power from the battery.
3. The buzzer will be louder.
   This is because the extra cell will provide more power to the buzzer.
4. From left to right: 3, 2, 4, 1.
5. The motor will spin faster in this circuit because the extra cell delivers more power to the motor.
   The motor will spin slower in this circuit because the buzzer uses up some of the power of the cell.

6.

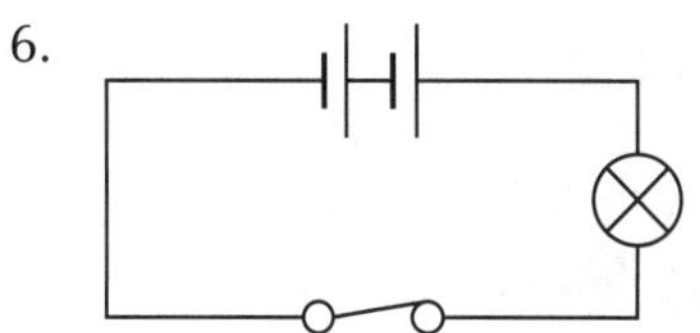

Any two from: e.g. remove one of the cells.
/ Change a cell for one with a lower voltage.
/ Add another component.
The voltage was too high so the bulb burned out.

Page 39 – End of Topic Quiz

1.

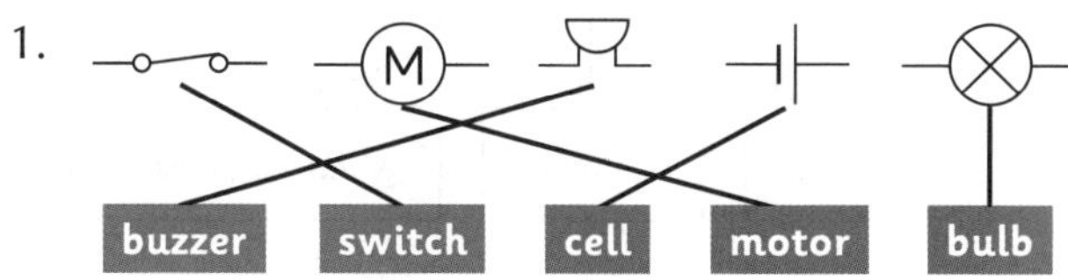

(4 marks for all five lines correct, otherwise 1 mark for each line that's correct.)

2. Adding more cells/batteries to the circuit makes the bulb brighter.
   Adding more bulbs to the circuit makes each bulb dimmer.
   The higher the voltage of the cell, the brighter the bulb will be.
   (1 mark for each correct answer)
3. You should have ticked:
   Add another cell to the circuit.
   Change a cell for one with a higher voltage.
   (1 mark for each correct answer)

Pages 40-45 – End of Year Test

1. Your blood absorbs nutrients and water through the gut.
   Your kidneys remove waste food products from your blood.
   When blood passes through your lungs, it absorbs oxygen from the air and gets rid of waste carbon dioxide.
   (1 mark for each correct answer)
2. You should have ticked:

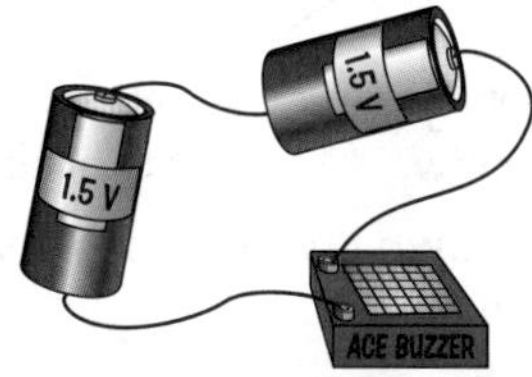

(1 mark)

This circuit has more batteries so the buzzer will receive more power. *(1 mark)*

3. Drinking too much ALCOHOL is bad for your LIVER, HEART and stomach. *(1 mark)*
   Humans need to eat a BALANCED diet to get the right amount of different NUTRIENTS. *(1 mark)*
   EXERCISE is important because it STRENGTHENS your muscles and helps to develop your LUNGS. *(1 mark)*

Answers

4. artery
capillaries
lung
muscle
heart
vein

(1 mark for each correct answer)
To pump blood to all parts of the body *(1 mark)*.

5.

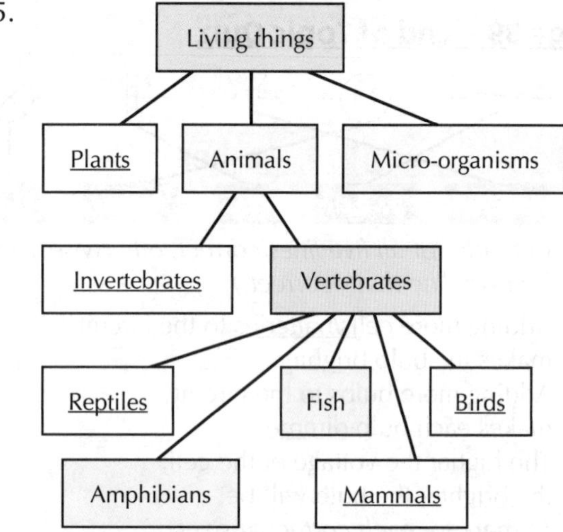

(1 mark for each correct answer)

6. Fossils can show us what ORGANISMS looked like MILLIONS of years ago. This means they can show us how plants and animals alive TODAY have EVOLVED.
(2 marks for all words filled in correctly, otherwise 1 mark for at least two words filled in correctly.)
E.g. there are lots of fossils that haven't been found / not all ancient living things formed fossils *(1 mark)*.

7. You should have circled: True, True, False
(1 mark for each correct answer)

8.

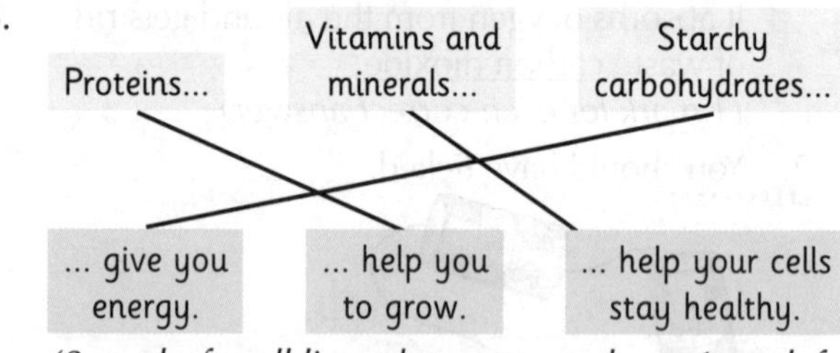

(2 marks for all lines drawn correctly, or 1 mark for at least one line drawn correctly.)

9. E.g.:

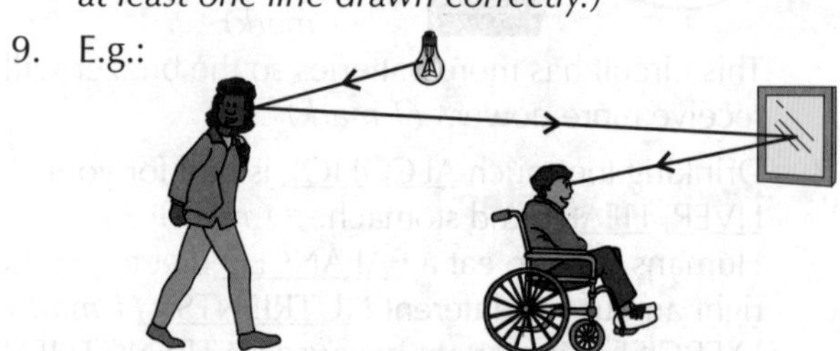

(1 mark for drawing three lines correctly, 1 mark for drawing the arrows in the correct directions.)

10. You should have circled: adaptation *(1 mark)*
E.g. they help a dolphin to swim to escape predators / catch prey *(1 mark)*.
When the dolphin-like animals started to swim to look for food, those animals with wider, flatter legs were likely to be better at swimming, so were more likely to survive and reproduce. Their offspring were likely to have inherited their parents' wide, flat legs, and so were also more likely to survive. Over time, a large number of the animals would have had legs like flippers that helped survival.
(2 marks for all words circled correctly, otherwise 1 mark for at least two words circled correctly.)

11. You should have circled: *(1 mark)*
insects *(1 mark)*
Any two from: e.g. six legs / body made up of three parts / one pair of antennae / an external skeleton. *(1 mark for each correct answer)*

12. Name: switch *(1 mark)*
Opening and closing / shutting this component controls the flow of electricity. *(1 mark)*
Name: buzzer *(1 mark)*
This component makes a sound / noise when electricity e.g. flows through it. *(1 mark)*

13. The sandcastle is opaque so it stops light from the Sun reaching the ground *(1 mark)*. Light travels past the sandcastle in straight lines, so the outline of the shadow has the same shape as the sandcastle *(1 mark)*.

14. The features of a living thing are its characteristics. Some characteristics are inherited, which means they are passed from parents to offspring. Living things that are closely related share lots of characteristics but they are not identical — the differences between them are called variation.
(1 mark for each correct answer)

15. E.g.:

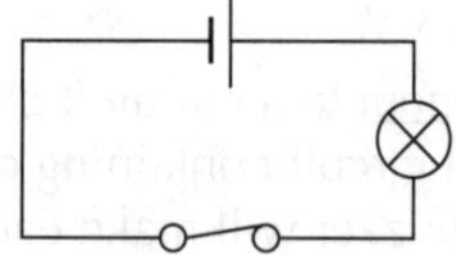

(1 mark for all three component symbols drawn correctly, 1 mark for the components being drawn correctly in a circuit with the switch closed.)
The bulb will be dimmer *(1 mark)* because the voltage of the cell is lower, so the bulb doesn't get as much power *(1 mark)*.

Glossary

Adaptation	A <u>characteristic</u> of an organism that helps it to survive in its <u>habitat</u>.
Alcohol	A <u>drug</u> that's found in some drinks like wine and beer. If you drink too much it can damage your <u>heart</u>, <u>liver</u> and <u>stomach</u>.
Amphibian	A type of <u>vertebrate</u> that is born with gills and develops lungs as it grows. The adult lays its eggs in water but can live on land.
Artery	A <u>blood vessel</u> which carries blood <u>away</u> from the heart.
Bird	A type of <u>vertebrate</u> that lays its eggs on land and has wings and feathers.
Blood	The <u>red liquid</u> that's pumped around the body by the <u>heart</u>. It <u>transports</u> nutrients, water and oxygen, as well as waste products.
Capillary	A <u>blood vessel</u> that lets things move <u>in</u> and <u>out</u> of the blood.
Cell	A source of <u>power</u> in an electrical circuit. Cells are sometimes called batteries.
Characteristic	A <u>feature</u> of an organism. For example, freckles are a characteristic of some humans.
Circuit diagram	A picture that uses <u>circuit symbols</u> to show all the <u>components</u> in a <u>circuit</u> and how they're <u>connected</u>.
Circulatory system	The system that <u>transports</u> substances around the body in the <u>blood</u>.
Classification key	A set of questions used to <u>identify</u> an organism.
Component	Something that <u>does a job</u> in a <u>circuit</u>, e.g. a bulb or a buzzer.
Drug	A substance that <u>changes</u> how the <u>body works</u>.
Evolution	How living things <u>change</u> over <u>time</u>.
Fish	A type of <u>vertebrate</u> that has gills and scales, and lays its eggs in water.
Fossil	The <u>shape</u> of a <u>long dead</u> animal or plant, found in a <u>rock</u>.
Habitat	Where an organism <u>lives</u>.

Glossary

Heart	The organ that pumps blood around the body.
Inheritance	When characteristics get passed on from a parent to its offspring.
Invertebrate	An animal without a backbone.
Light ray	A beam of light. Light always travels in straight lines.
Light source	Something that gives out its own light.
Mammal	A type of vertebrate that has hair or fur and gives birth to live babies.
Micro-organism	A very tiny living thing, e.g. bacteria.
Nicotine	A chemical in tobacco that is addictive, so people who smoke find it hard to stop even if they want to.
Nutrients	Substances that a plant or animal needs to live and grow.
Offspring	The children of a living thing.
Organ	Part of an organism that has a special job, e.g. the heart.
Organism	A living thing. All plants and animals are organisms.
Periscope	A tube with mirrors in it that allows you to see things that are out of sight — for example, it allows you to see over walls or around corners.
Reflection	When light bounces off a surface.
Reptile	A type of vertebrate that has scales and lays its eggs on land.
Shadow	A dark area made when light rays are blocked by an object.
Solvent (drug)	Substances that you inhale, e.g. glues and paints, which can be addictive and can damage your brain.
Tobacco	A substance that is found in cigarettes and cigars. Smoking it can cause heart disease, lung cancer and breathing problems.
Variation	Differences between living things.
Vein	A blood vessel that takes blood back to the heart.
Vertebrate	An animal with a backbone.
Voltage	A measure of the amount of power something has. For example, the higher the voltage of a battery, the more power it has.